Bitterroot Gold

To Randy
Where the trail leads to
the high Country.

Best wishes

Monty Spears

December 24th
2009

D1160913

Bitterroot Gold

Monty C. Spears

VANTAGE PRESS
New York

Published by Vantage Press, Inc.
516 West 34th Street, New York, New York 10001

Manufactured in the United States of America
ISBN: 0-533-12196-5

Library of Congress Catalog Card No.: 96-90862

0 9 8 7 6 5 4 3 2

I would like to dedicate this book to my grandfather Lloyd Rupe, who was among the first pioneers in the Bitterroot Mountains. It was on a fishing trip in these mountains that he first told me of the Magruder murders.

Contents

Acknowledgments

I want to thank Brenda Trautman for the time and energy that she put in helping with this book. Without her, it would not have been published.

She has always been there, helping me through the many rough spots I've encountered while on one adventure or the other.

I want to thank John "Boy" Weber for his mountain man face that gives the character to the cover of this book.

John has long been my friend and hunting partner. We have shared many campfires and he feels the spirit of the Bitterroots as I do.

1

Grandpa's Moose

Marty Kincade wasn't exactly the Tom Sawyer or Huckleberry Finn type, but he was a unique twelve-year-old. Marty lived in the small mountain community of Grangeville, Idaho, with his parents. He was an average student, but with his obsessive inquisitiveness and love of the mountains and wildlife, he rarely found time for his homework or household chores.

Marty's grandfather, Lloyd Rupp, wasn't much help in encouraging the studies Marty needed to do. In fact, John Kincade, Marty's father, felt Lloyd was the sole cause of Marty neglecting his schoolwork. Marty was more than just a grandson. Marty was Lloyd's hunting and fishing partner. Consequently, Lloyd shuttled Marty away from his school and parents, perhaps more than should have been allowed. Geneva, Marty's mother, and Lloyd's daughter, just couldn't say no to either her father or her son. Marty's father couldn't say no to Geneva. Therefore, Lloyd and Marty were usually able to partake in all the hunting, fishing, and adventure they cared to find.

Marty's younger brother and sister, Roger and Julie Kincade, were consequently more proficient in house and garden chores than their older brother. The younger children didn't seem to mind, but John was resenting Marty's lack of responsibility and his grandfather's enabling of that defect.

1

For Marty, though, there wasn't enough adventure in life.

Two events would occur in the fall of 1957 that would leave a memorable milestone in the life of Marty Kincade.

Both events would affect his life, but the one he figured was the biggest event would fade with time and in later years become little more than a subject of reminiscing. The other event would develop into a continued and growing interest that would take Marty Kincade on one of the wildest and most dangerous adventures of his life.

The biggest event, for Marty, happened in September of that year. Lloyd was drawn for a moose permit and had asked Marty to go with him. Marty was in school, but after several hours of begging and pleading, he finally convinced his parents to let him go with his grandfather and take a few days off.

John probably wouldn't have consented, but with Lloyd pushing and Marty pulling, Geneva Kincade had finally been swayed as usual. In turn, she convinced John to let their son go with her father. The very next day they left.

Lloyd and Marty had traveled three hours from Lloyd's small ranch at Harpster, Idaho, and made camp near American River. "Damn good moose country," Lloyd would say from that time on. Lloyd found a spot sixty yards from the river, where he spied moose droppings and parked his brand new '57 Chevrolet pickup truck. "This place will do, Boy," Lloyd said. "Lotta sign herebouts and we can catch trout in the mornin' fer breakfast."

"Yah, Grandpa. I love it here. Better than school, that's fer sure!" Marty spouted.

Lloyd chuckled and said, "Take all the gear out o' the back and I'll start the stove and cook some soup."

After lunch, Lloyd sent Marty to gather wood for the campfire while he blew up air mattresses and made their beds in the back of the pickup. Lloyd had built an "A" frame with a tin roof over the bed of the pickup. Over this, he pulled a sixteen-foot tarp, which was long enough for a cooking area in back of the pickup, if you used the tail gate for the stove and two poles for the end of the tarp. This was Lloyd's version of the camper.

They spent a leisurely evening around the campfire, making plans for the next day's hunt and the prospects of bagging a moose. Marty knew you just didn't "go out" and shoot a moose. He had killed his first deer two years before, after several days of hunting. He had helped his grandpa and uncle pack it back to their truck and was well aware of the work involved.

He had to admit, though, he didn't know if Grandpa could pack a moose or not, but he knew he couldn't. He had seen only one moose before and knew it was bigger than an elk, and he had seen a lot of those.

Lloyd turned out their lantern and crawled inside his sleeping bag. Marty wasn't sleepy. He was wide awake, with hundreds of questions bouncing around in his head.

"Grandpa, you think you'll get a moose tomorrow?"

"Yep."

"How you gonna pack him out?"

"I've got a friend with horses."

"Can I shoot the moose?"

"No, Boy, you can't."

"Grandpa, what's all those tall piles of yellow rock stacked up on both sides of the river?"

"It's rock piled up by the miners back in the old days, during the Gold Rush."

Marty thought about this for a few moments. . . . Then, "Did the miners have to shoot at claim jumpers in the old days?"

"Yep, and some o' them got shot at as well."

"Grandpa, tell me a story about a miners' shoot-out."

"Boy, how old are you gonna be next month?"

"Thirteen, Grandpa. Why?"

"'Cause you're gonna become a teenager before you go to sleep if you keep carryin' on like ye are." Lloyd grunted, as he turned over in his bag and fluffed his pillow.

Marty reflected on that for a while as he looked up at the sky and watched "ORION" fight the lion. His eyelids started to get heavy. "I wonder if Orion was a real guy in the Roman days? I wonder if he ever killed a moose or picked up rocks looking for gold?"

Marty was awakened the next morning by the sounds of Lloyd pumping the gas stove. Umphesssst, umphesssst, umphesssst.

"What you want fer breakfast, Boy?" Lloyd asked, as he noticed Marty sit up and rub his eyes.

"I guess cereal or French toast, Grandpa."

"Got none o' that stuff, but I'll have you bacon, eggs 'n toast in a minute."

It was starting to turn daylight when they finished breakfast. Marty could see the dim yellow rock pilings along the river and he could make out treetops on the various ridges around camp.

Lloyd loaded his .270 Winchester and looked at Marty. Neither said anything. They just started up a ridge. After all, Marty was a two-year veteran, with two whitetail deer to his credit. Lloyd was proud of the boy and he knew the boy thought his grandfather *walked on water*.

They moved silently up the ridge for the better part of an hour. Then, just before reaching the ridge top, Lloyd started slowly cutting the finger ridges while watching the crest. Marty quietly pulled pine needles and, as Lloyd had shown him in times past, broke and rubbed them behind his ears and on his wrist. "Everywhere you got a pulse, Boy, that's where you rub 'em." Marty quietly mouthed his grandfather's words, as he worked the "pine scent" into his skin.

Although "savvy" for a twelve-year-old hunter, Marty still had the immaturity and impatience of a twelve-year-old boy. They had stopped so Lloyd could scope a ridge in front of them that was mostly vacant of trees, but did hold a variety of brush, including "yew" wood, a favorite food of the moose. After several minutes of inactivity, Marty started throwing small sticks and pine cones at a squirrel that decided to really "scold them." Marty was annoyed and became more so when the noisy squirrel wouldn't shut up, even after being "thumped" by a well-thrown pine cone.

"Do you see him, Boy?" Lloyd quietly spoke.

"Yah, he just ran up the tree further."

"No, Boy, I mean the moose," Lloyd said, "a bull and two cows. I seen his head a while ago. He's big, real big."

Marty threw the remainder of his pine cones away and crossed over a log to his grandpa's side. "Where? Where? I don't see 'em."

"'Bout two hundred yards out, Boy, on that open ridge just under that big bunch o' alder berry bushes and a little to the right."

Marty studied the ridge a few moments and then, he too, saw them. Just after Marty saw them, the bull stepped out into the open and started feeding on the alder berry. Lloyd said, "I can take him from here. I'll use the log as a rest."

Marty thought the moose so ugly that it was beautiful. "Look how he moves, Grandpa. Kind of with a clop, clop, clop and he's gruntin'. Hear 'im?"

Lloyd was preoccupied with finding a firing position and wasn't paying attention to the details of the moose's activity. He should have. No sooner had Lloyd turned his back and stepped back across the log, when the moose decided to pay attention to the squirrel, who, by this time, had two of his buddies joining the protest.

The bull, deciding that this ridge was too crowded and noisy, started trotting down the ridge, heading for the safety of the tree line. Lloyd started moving quickly. "Watch 'em, Boy. See where he goes when I shoot." Lloyd ran to a stump and jumped up on it. He could now see the bull clearly, running at a full gallop. Both cows were close behind.

Lloyd threw the .270 to his shoulder and centered the cross hairs of his scope behind the big, black shoulder. Boom—the bull continued to run. Lloyd centered the cross hairs again. Boom—the bull continued almost to the trees! Lloyd centered the cross hairs for the third time. Boom—the bull entered the trees, with the cows right behind him.

"Damn! I hope I didn't miss him. He didn't act like he was hit."

"Yah, he did, Grandpa, he flinched all three times, just like my first deer."

"Are you sure? I didn't see him do that!"

"I'm sure, Grandpa. I saw 'em."

"Okay. Let's give him a little time and we'll look fer a blood trail."

It took them fifteen minutes to reach the area where the moose had been. Marty marveled at how different the hillside looked when you were on it. He didn't see anything at first. Then he could see where the ground had been torn up, "more like plowed up," and blood, lots of it, all over the ground and on the bushes.

"See, Gramps? I told you, you got him," Marty said.

"Yep, Boy. You sure did. Must be your eyes are keener 'n mine. Guess I'm getting old."

"You're not old, Grandpa. You got the bull."

"Yah. Well, we got to track him now. Hope he keeps goin' down hill. He's headed fer the river and our camp's only half a mile below us."

"Maybe if we yell and run after him, he'll run down and

jump in the back of the truck," Marty said, more serious than not.

"Not likely. 'Spect he'll run a mite, then lay down. We'll follow 'em and see. You stay back in case I have to shoot again."

They followed the bull downhill to the river and across. On the side of a large yellow rock pile lay a dead, very large bull moose.

The following week capped the most exciting adventure of young Marty's life. The *Idaho County Freepress*, at Grangeville, covered the hunt. On the front page was Lloyd and Marty's picture, with the moose. The headline caption read: "WHOPPER MOOSE. TAKEN BY MR. LLOYD RUPP OF HARPSTER." The story went on to say that Lloyd was accompanied by his grandson, Marty Kincade, who was the son of Mr. & Mrs. John Kincade of Grangeville. The moose had an antler spread of 50 inches and field dressed at 1,100 pounds.

Marty was the envy of all the boys at school and truly loved bragging on his grandpa, who was the best hunter in all of Idaho. No one disputed that. After all, the bull was the state record in 1957.

2

A Killer and a Story

The second and more important event in Marty's life occurred a month after the moose hunt. This event Marty would remember well. This event happened on October 20th, his birthday. He was thirteen years old when this adventure started. He would be forty-seven when it ended.

Most folks in Harpster considered Lloyd Rupp a far better than average hunter. His grandson, Marty, considered him the best hunter ever and just about the best at everything else. On opening day of elk season, Lloyd had killed a big six-point bull near their cabin at McComas Meadows. Last week, Lloyd and Marty had each taken a five-point whitetail buck near the meadows. Marty was on a high that never seemed to end when he was with his grandfather.

Lloyd had put Marty on a stand between two ridges that had been clear cut a couple years before. "Stay right here, Boy," Lloyd had instructed. "Lotta bucks in the brush just the other side o' these ridges. I'm gonna circle and come up through that stand o' trees. If'n there's something in thar, they'll come a-scooting on one or both o' these ridges, so keep yer eyes peeled."

Lloyd had been gone a half hour when Marty heard his grandfather shoot. Marty's heart started beating faster. He felt like his heart was going to bounce right out of his chest. He couldn't stay on the stump he had found, because he felt like he had to go to the bathroom. He got down, shifting his weight from one foot to the other. Just as he decided to relieve himself, he saw it, a large five-point whitetail, coming around the ridge right at him. The buck had his head stuck out and his tail stuck between his legs, much like a pup-dog in trouble would.

Marty put the bead of his iron sights behind the front shoulders of the deer as it quartered away from him. Boom— the buck fell sideways downhill, regained its feet, and fell again. It stayed down this time and Marty was elated. He had not shot a buck before and this fellow was big.

Marty dressed the buck and was removing the scent glands from the hocks like Lloyd had previously shown him when Lloyd yelled from a ridge top, "How'dya do?"

"Got one, Grandpa, a big one!"

"Got one up here, too. I'll be down in a few minutes," Lloyd replied.

Lloyd and Marty had spent a great deal of the summer and fall hunting and fishing. Marty knew this weekend would be his last fishing trip of the year with his grandfather. He also knew he would not have been able to come on this fishing trip, had it not been his birthday weekend. John, his father, had been grumbling about his grades and his not bringing any homework home from school. John at first refused to let Marty go on the fishing trip, explaining that Marty needed to use this time for his studies. Like other times, Geneva intervened on Marty's behalf. John never could refuse his wife, so Marty and Lloyd were off again.

As they left the driveway, John said, "Honey, we can't always let that boy have his way."

"Oh, hon, it's his birthday, and besides, it's the last trip of the year for the two of them. Daddy really enjoys Marty's company. In fact, I think he would be real lonely without him.

They have become real close sidekicks."

John terminated the conversation with a "Yah, well," as he turned and went back inside the house.

John Kincade had been brought up with responsibility and it bothered him when others around him were not responsible, especially when "others" meant his son. It made John feel that he wasn't being responsible in directing Marty's upbringing. But he couldn't refuse Geneva. Never could, never would.

After leaving Grangeville, Lloyd looked at Marty and grinned. He said, "Don't think your Pa is none to happy 'bout us agoin' fishing agin." Marty, riding shotgun in the pickup, just looked out the window and said nothing. Lloyd continued, "Guess I do feel a little guilty, taking you most every weekend and sometimes during the week. How's your studies? Are ye passin' yer studies?"

"Most of 'em," Marty replied. "I'd rather go huntin' and fishing anyways. Learn a whole bunch more. I don't like stupid school!"

"What classes you havin' trouble in?" Lloyd asked.

"Math and English, Math and English," Marty repeated. "Always the same two subjects. I had to take my English class over and I'm the only boy in it. Rest are stupid girls."

Lloyd asked, "You don't like girls?"

"No. They're stupid."

"You think that now, Boy, but just you wait a year or so. You'll like 'em plenty then. Probably quit huntin' and fishin' with me when you find yerself a girl."

"NO SIR, Grandpa! Girls are just stupid, they don't like nothin' that's fun. I like to do things that is exciting."

"Jest you wait, Boy, girls will be plenty exciting fer you one o' these days. They got ways to make a man feel real good, and besides, if it wasn't fer girls and women folk, you and I wouldn't be here."

Marty thought on that awhile. After a few minutes, he turned in the seat, facing his grandfather, and with a very solemn expression and low serious voice, he asked, "How does babies get in girls' stomachs, Grandpa?"

Lloyd swallowed hard. This wasn't his specialty. After a moment or so of clearing his throat, Lloyd said, "You remember that old one-horn bull o' mine and what he did to that cow last year?"

Marty said, "Yeeeah, you mean when he jumped up on her and put his peter in her?"

Lloyd cleared his throat again. "Yep, that's what I mean. That's what dads do to moms, then a baby is born just like a cow has a calf. That's what all critters do to have young."

Marty thought a moment. "Yuk. . . . What do you say to a girl when you jump up on her, Grandpa?"

Lloyd bit his tongue. "Let's talk about fishin', Boy. We're headed fer Newsome Creek. Remember where that's at? We passed it when we went to American River after that moose. First, we're gonna stop at the Meadows cabin. I got to pick up some more fishin' gear."

Lloyd hoped the boy wouldn't ask any more questions. He had run out of things to say.

After leaving Lloyd's cabin at McComas Meadows, they drove over a mountain and dropped into the Newsome Creek drainage. Twenty minutes later they were at Newsome Creek.

Marty loved Newsome Creek, it looked a lot like American River. It had the same crystal-clear water, with yellow-and-white rock piles up and down both sides of the creek. "I see the miners have been here, too. Huh, Grandpa?"

"Yep, sure were, Boy. Let's camp in the old way-station, over there across the creek."

"What's a way-station, Grandpa?"

"It's where folks rested up a bit and got something to eat, while they were aheadin' in and out to the gold camps. The wagon road followed the old Nez Perce Indian Trail a lot o' the way. When the miners would get to these stations all along the route, they would rest up and take care o' the horses and do whatever they had to do. When I was a small boy, I went over it a time or two with my dad, your great-grandpa."

"What was his name, Grandpa?"

"Smith," Lloyd said.

"No, I mean his first name, Grandpa."

"That was his first name, Smith, Smith Rupp," Lloyd said.

"What happened to him, Grandpa? Did he die?"

"Yep, in 1923 he was pizened, murdered."

"He was? Tell me about it!"

"Later," Lloyd said. "Let's get camp set up and do some fishin' first."

The old way-station was about six feet in height and about twelve feet wide. The floor was covered with old straw left by another traveler. Marty walked in and immediately smelled a strong, musty smell. He noticed that the far right corner housed a stack of small sticks and twigs with moss, string and old pieces of rope. There was even a pop can and an old beer bottle wedged into the pile.

"Gag! What's that smell? It's awful!"

Lloyd, coming through the door behind Marty, said, "Yep! Wood rat! That pile o' sticks is his nest."

"I don't know if I want to sleep in here with that rat, Grandpa."

"Well, guess I don't either, Boy. I was jest athinkin' thet maybe we could stay one night, like I did years ago with my dad, when I was yer age. Don't make no difference no how, we'll sleep in the pickup."

Marty followed Lloyd back out to the pickup, where they started unloading the camping equipment. "How come you stayed here with your dad and how come that building is so short?"

"Well." Lloyd pondered on which question to answer first. "The building is short 'cause they didn't stay in buildings much those days. They slept in them and ate, 'n that's 'bout all. The folks around here was either mining the river or travelin' through to other gold fields, like Elk City, Florence, Dixie, Bufflar Hump, the Gospels, or even as far back as Virginia City, Montana. They jest wasn't time fer folks to be hangin' around buildings. No need o' it. Why, they wasn't even radios to listen to in those days."

"Hand me that Coleman stove, Boy. I'll put it on the stump yonder and we'll make our kitchen thar, 'cause it's close to the creek."

Marty gave Lloyd the stove and followed him to the stump with the box of kitchen utensils. "No radios, huh? Well, we even got television now, Grandpa! Our neighbors got one last month and Dad said we could get one next year. I even watched a picture show on one, called *Starlit Stairway*. The picture came from Spokane and it was about two girls my age a-tap-dancing. The girls were stupid, but they danced real good."

"Yep, I heerd o' that television, too. Guess some folks really like 'em," Lloyd said.

"What was you here for when you was my age, Grandpa?" Marty asked for the second time.

Lloyd put the Coleman on the stump and arranged the kitchen utensils and frying pans next to it.

"Thet was the first time I was here. Been through here lotta times since then. Then Dad and I come through here. We was aheadin' to Elk City to go a-huntin' with some o' our kin folk thet lived thar. I'd say thet was around 1905. This was the only road in these parts at that time. It was built in 1895."

"What was you here for the other times, Grandpa?"

"Oh, different things, takin' supplies to miners, pastured a bunch o' cattle into Red River one summer, did a little trap-

13

pin' fer a couple o' years and jest a lot o' huntin' and fishin'.

"A few years later, they built the old Elk City Wagon Road and more way-stations. Newsome here was one o' the main ones. The travelers stayed all night here when the stage line started from Stites to Elk City.

"If'n you started a stage trip from Stites to Elk City in those days, it took you two days to make it. Why, now it'd take less than two hours. I remember takin' the stage one time, from Stites to Elk City. We left Stites at 6:00 A.M. and got to Mountain House at noon. Mountain House is right up there by my cabin at McComas Meadows. Remember? We went a-huntin' up thar last year and camped at Mountain House."

"Yea, I think so," Marty said.

"Anyway, we got here to Newsome right at dark. It was pretty slow with horses those days, but ye did get to study the country a mite better 'n ye do now days. Some o' the other way-stations was called Mud Springs, Switchback, Riebold Station, Clearwater, Nolan Station, and Corral Hill. They were scattered along the old wagon road, which is right along side the old Nez Perce Indian Trail in a lot o' places. Guess maybe I already told ye that, though. Sometimes I get to rattlin' on so much I must sound like a preacher man or maybe a schoolteacher trying to learn ye somethin'."

"I like this kinda learnin', Grandpa. It's better'n school any day!" Marty exclaimed.

"Let's get our fish poles, Boy, and do what we came here to do. The cutthroat is a-waitin' to be caught."

Lloyd said that he would go down the creek, so Marty decided to go up the creek. Lloyd had mentioned beaver ponds about a mile up, so Marty decided he would try those first, then fish back down the creek to camp.

After twenty minutes, Marty reached the ponds. Even though he was twelve years old, thirteen tomorrow, he still marveled at the majestic beauty of Newsome Creek and its drainage area. Marty observed the Gospels to the south. High blue mountains, with snow-capped peaks distinguishing them from surrounding mountains. Newsome Creek, in the foreground, almost looked blue from a distance, but once you were close, the stream was crystal clear. Just above the beaver ponds, Newsome Creek split around a small island with a lone pine tree, then came back together. The immediate area around the creek was heavily timbered, with marshy meadows every few hundred yards. Although fir trees were plentiful in the area, Marty was amazed at the strong, pleasant smell of pine. Marty loved the mountains and fully intended to learn everything he could about them and the animals that lived there.

Marty often wished he had been born in his grandfather's time, when you found no cars and few people. He would often have this wish throughout his life. He daydreamed all the while he fished.

They heard the car a long time before they actually saw it. They finished cleaning their trout before the car finally came into view. Lloyd had started to build a campfire and Marty was shaking the fish in a paper sack containing flour when the old gray Buick pulled up alongside of Lloyd's pickup and stopped. Marty heard his grandfather swear under his breath. He had only heard him use that word one other time. The time when someone had stolen all of his guns from the cabin at McComas Meadows.

Marty knew his grandfather must not like the man in the Buick. Lloyd's face had contorted into an almost frown.

Marty noted the man as he got out of the car. He appeared to be about sixty years old. He wore round wire-rim glasses and a felt hat with a short brim. He was dressed in blue-and-white striped bibbed overalls. The only thing unusual about the man was that he wore a pistol, but that itself wasn't unusual, at least not in the Idaho Mountains. It was where he wore it that Marty thought was odd. The pistol, held by an old, brown, nearly worn through belt, was positioned squarely in the man's crotch. The belt also held a large bone-handled hunting knife, which was on the man's left side.

"Howdy, Lloyd," the man said as he shut his car door. "How's the fishing?"

"Good enough, George," Lloyd replied. "What brings you up herebouts?"

"Oh, probably same as you, thought I'd do a little fishing. Maybe camp in the old way-station, if you are not using it."

Lloyd said, "Nope, we're not a-usin' it. Wood rat got there first and I don't like rats."

The man laughed. "Well, I don't mind rats, fact of the matter is, lotta folks think I'm a rat." The man laughed again, only arrogantly this time.

"Talk to you after while, Lloyd. I'm gonna set up camp first, won't be long before dark. Who's the boy, Lloyd?"

"My grandson. Marty Kincade," Lloyd replied.

"How do, Boy, my name's George Timick. Your grandfather helped me outta some trouble one time. We go back aways, don't we, Lloyd?"

Timick turned, got back in his car, and backed over to the way-station, where he started unloading his camping equipment. Marty could see the man had fishing gear.

"That guy's kinda stupid, Grandpa, the whole time he was talking to you, he had both his hands resting on his gun butt. The barrel was tilted right into his peter. If his gun went off, he wouldn't jump up on any girls, would he, Grandpa?"

Lloyd chuckled. "No, guess he wouldn't, Boy."

They ate the trout that night without talking much. After the dishes were washed, Marty asked. "Grandpa, what'd that Mr. Timick mean that you helped him outta trouble?"

Lloyd, who was sitting on a wood chunk and smoking

16

his pipe, looked across the campfire at his grandson. He took the pipe out of his mouth and tapped the bowl on a fire circle rock. Lloyd thought for a while then said, "A few years back, George was arrested by the law in Grangeville, fer killing a man and woman."

"Wow! How come he's not in jail?" Marty asked.

"Well, hold on and I'll tell you why. I was on the jury that heard his case. We all thought he was guilty, but about half o' us was not convinced beyond a reasonable doubt that he was. I was one o' the people who wasn't totally convinced and I was also the jury foreman. That's why he thinks I helped him out o' trouble. I didn't, though. Deep down I suspected and still do, that he killed those folks. It's jest that I wasn't positive like the judge told us we had to be."

Marty looked over to Timick's campfire and watched him cooking his dinner. "Wow, there's a killer at Newsome Creek."

Marty didn't sleep much that night and when he did, it was fitful. He also made Lloyd's sleep less than sound, with his constant turning and moaning. He didn't remember most of his dreams that night, but what he did remember caused him to keep an eye on George Timick all that next day.

"You slept like a green broke colt last night, Boy! What is wrong with ye? I's bout ready to send ye over to Timick's camp."

Marty gave his grandfather a sideways glance. "He's the one kept me awake, Grandpa. Last night I saw him walking toward our campfire. I was a-layin' on the ground beside it. I could see his blue-and-white striped pants, where they were tucked into his boot tops. I looked a little higher 'n saw his gun holster still in his crotch, 'cept there was no gun in it. I looked a little higher and saw his hand with the gun in it and he pointed it down at us while we were a-layin' by the fire. I couldn't do nothin', it was like I was stuck to the ground."

Lloyd nodded, understanding. "Well, don't think we have to worry about George. He ain't got nothin' 'gain us, but I know how dreams can be real sometimes. I remember a huntin' trip that I dreamed about one time."

"Tell me about it, Grandpa."

Lloyd thought, as he rummaged through the gear, looking for the Coleman white gas to put in the camp stove. "Well, I was a-huntin' bar one time with my hounds. I was a kid, jest a little older 'n ye are now. Was a-huntin' up on old Blacktail Mountain, ye know, up by the McComas Meadows where our cabin is? Anyways, the hounds treed an old sow bar. When I got to the tree, I tied the hounds to me with my boot laces, so's they wouldn't mix with the bar when I shot it out o' the tree. I shot her out o' the tree all right, an soon as she hit the ground, the hounds took off, a-pullin' me right along with them. It would have been all right, 'cept we were on a side hill and the hounds caught up with that old she bar right quick like, and down the hill we went. That ole she bar was only wounded. Now you talk about dreams. Try dreamin' bout thet little sashay a time or two."

Marty, wide-eyed and at full attention, asked, "Gosh. What did you do, Grandpa?"

Lloyd, who acted very serious, said, "Why, hell fire, Boy, I jest reached down thet old bar's throat, grabbed her by the tail, and pulled her inside out. She jest took off a-runnin', back up the hill from whence she came."

Marty sat motionless, with his mouth open. Mixed emotion and thought whirled inside his head. Finally, "Come on, Grandpa, tell me a true story. Tell me a true story, maybe a story 'bout the old days, where there was a lot o' shootin' and stuff."

Lloyd howled and rocked back and forth with laughter. A stream of tobacco juice ran out the side of his mouth and down his chin.

Marty continued to look at his grandfather, with a little irritation. George Timick looked up from his campfire by the way-station and wondered if Lloyd was laughing at him.

Finally, Lloyd quit laughing and resumed his task of filling the Coleman stove, so he could fix their breakfast. "Okay, Boy, I'll tell you a real-life shoot'em up story, after we eat breakfast, then fish a couple o' hours. I don't wanna miss mornin' fishin', 'cause it's best o' the day."

"What's the story 'bout, Grandpa?"

"'Bout a feller name o' Lloyd Magruder, who was kilt and robbed o' his gold. But I ain't gonna tell you any more 'bout it jest yet, 'cause it's a long story and I'm hungry right at the minute."

After breakfast, Lloyd and Marty grabbed their fishing poles and headed for the creek. Lloyd went upstream, toward the beaver ponds, while Marty went downstream.

As Marty was entering a wooded side of the stream, he looked back and saw his grandfather just before he disappeared around a bend in the creek. George Timick was about a hundred yards behind Lloyd, following him upstream, with fishing pole in hand.

Marty fished about an hour, and although he caught a rainbow every few minutes, he was losing interest. His thoughts were on Timick following his grandfather upstream. Finally, Marty could take it no longer. He wasn't going to sit there fishing while a killer with a gun followed his grandfather.

Marty ran back to camp as fast as he could. When he reached the pickup, he threw his fishing pole down and reached under his grandfather's sleeping bag in the back of the pickup. For a few moments, he marveled at the new J.C. Higgins .22 caliber rifle that his grandfather would give him for his birthday present. He searched a few moments for the ammunition and when he found it, he loaded the single shot weapon and took off on a dead run, dropping half of the bullets as he covered ground, not much slower than a whitetail deer would.

After a few moments, Marty reached the beaver ponds. He could hear voices. Thank God! Grandpa was still okay then. Marty climbed a rock piling that separated his side of the bank from the ponds. He moved very quietly as he raised the rifle to his shoulder. He would shoot Timick if his grandfather was hurt or about to be.

As Marty reached the top of the rock pile, Timick came into view directly below him. Marty cocked the rifle and centered the sights on Timick's back. He noticed his grandfather upstream about fifty feet from Timick. Both men were fishing and talking about his grandfather's state record bull moose.

In the next few moments, Marty also realized that Timick was not wearing his pistol belt. Slowly, he lowered the rifle and eased backward down the rock pile. His heart was beating so fast he could hear it.

"Crap!" he thought. He had almost shot Timick for doing nothing but fishing. Marty paused at the bottom of the rock pile, then turned and jogged back to camp.

What had he been thinking of? What had made him think Timick would hurt his grandfather? He felt strange about pointing a loaded gun at another human being. He had done something that his grandfather, uncles, and his father had always cautioned him never to do. *Never point a gun at anyone.*

Marty fished an orange soda, which he had brought as a present to himself on his birthday, out of Newsome Creek. Using a can opener, he opened the soda and drank half of it in three swallows. **Don't drink so much so fast,** his mother often told him. **If you drink beer like that when you get older, you'll be an alcoholic.**

"Okay, Mom," Marty said to himself. *"Damn!"* He

thought, *it makes a guy's throat dry to point a gun at some-one.* Marty jumped up on the fender of his grandfather's pick-up, and sipped the soda. Marty was still there when his grandfather returned from upstream.

"Yer back early, Boy. What'd ya do, run out a bait?" Lloyd asked.

"Naw, got thirsty for an orange soda, so I come on back."

"Yah, your ma told me you brought several fer yer birth-day. Sakes, Boy, how many o' those pops you gonna drink in one sittin'?" Lloyd asked, seeing three empty cans on the ground by the pickup and noticing that Marty had a fourth in his hand.

"This is my last one for now," Marty said. "Grandpa, can you tell me that story o' Magruder?"

"Yea, in a minute," Lloyd said. "First, I want to give you the present I got fer yer birthday." Lloyd walked back to the rear of the pickup, reached under his sleeping bag, and pulled out the rifle. He walked back to the front of the pickup, where Marty was sitting and handed it to him. Marty feigned sur-prise. "Before you go gettin' too surprised, do you need to un-load yer gun?"

Marty was surprised then. "How . . . how did you know, Grandpa?"

"Well, first ah all, last week after you helped me clean out the storage room, I found thet the gun had been taken out o' its box. It was put back all right, but not the way it should have been. It was put back by someone in a hurry and that fits you to a T. Mr. Patience ye are, Boy. Sides thet, yer ma or pa would have said somethin' 'bout my new rifle if'n they'd found it. It wasn't yer brother, Roger, fer he never goes into thet room, less you take 'em, and it wasn't yer Uncle Darrald, 'cause he would a said somethin' 'bout any gun he came across. You know him and guns. He's 'bout huntin' like you and me. Thet leaves only you. A snoopy, curious, impatient feller like you is the one thet found thet gun.

"Yesiree. You left as much sign as an ol' buck in the rut."

Marty thought about the day he found the gun in the storage room and how excited he was when he removed it from the box. He knew he must have put the gun in the box upside down because he heard his grandfather enter the house and he didn't want to get caught with his birthday present before he was supposed to have it.

Marty knew that he would find his birthday present in the storage room, because that is where his grandfather had put his birthday present for the last five years. That's where his grandfather put everyone's birthday present and Christmas presents.

Marty remembered that his Uncle Darrald had caught him and his brother, Roger, just before they had managed to open their Christmas presents two years ago. Their Uncle Darrald had opened the storage room, while he was removing some old boxes of books, and the two boys hurried inside, while he was putting the books in his pickup truck. He had returned while Marty was carefully removing the last strip of tape from a large box, which, as he found out later during Christmas, held his first cowboy hat. Their Uncle Darrald hadn't been pleased, but his reprimand had been gentle. Now here he was again, getting caught. Marty felt ashamed.

Lloyd continued, "While ago, on thet rock pile, you were quiet all right, but yer shadow gave you away. Remember how I showed you 'bout yer shadow when yer fishin' a stream? A shadow can scare fish. Same applies to huntin', if'n yer on a ridge or a rock pile, or huntin' beast or man. I was a lookin' fer fish shadows, when I saw yourin's. Ol' George didn't see ye, 'cause he was a lookin' downstream. Good thing too, 'cause he would probably been a little upset, you pointin' a gun and all, at 'em."

Marty was really ashamed. He couldn't look his grandfather in the face.

"I'm sorry, Grandpa," Marty said. "I thought maybe old Timick was fixin' to shoot you, like he did those folks in Grangeville."

Lloyd looked at his grandson, his face softened from its firm expression. He spoke in a voice so low that it was almost a whisper. "I know why you did it, Boy. I guess maybe the same thought crossed my mind. But, Boy, a man's gotta be careful when he points a gun at a feller. Maybe you should have just snuck up and looked things over a mite, 'fore you started pullin' guns on people."

"I know, Grandpa," Marty said. A large tear rolled down his cheek. He lowered his head and couldn't find anything else to say. He knew he had disappointed his grandfather, the last thing on earth that he wanted to do.

"Aw heck, Boy." Lloyd put his arm around Marty's shoulder. "Come on over here an sit on this log. I'll stoke up the campfire and tell ye about this Magruder feller."

Lloyd added a few dry twigs and some larger wood chunks to the embers of that morning's campfire and sat down on the log beside Marty.

"What I'm 'bout to tell ye, Boy, is a true story. It's about violence at its very ugliest. This story has also had effect on my life and maybe the tellin' o' it can he'p you 'bout yer learnin' o' life's ways. Maybe what I'm 'bout to tell ye will have an effect on yer life as well."

"How long ago did this story happen, Grandpa?" Marty asked, feeling a little better now that his interest was stirred.

"Happened in October o' 1863," Lloyd said, "just a few days before your birthday, ninety-four years ago."

"Wow" Marty said. "That's almost a hundred years ago."

"Yep, 'n thet gold has been just a-layin' out thar in those hills waitin' fer some feller to come along and find it, but no one ever has."

"What gold, Grandpa?"

"The gold out thar in the Bitterroot Mountains thet the bandits hid after they kilt Magruder and his men. Bitterroot Gold," Lloyd said. "Thet's what most folks call it here 'bouts, anyways."

"Wow! Tell me about it, Grandpa," Marty almost yelled.

"I am a-tellin' you, boy, if'n ye'll jest listen a mite so's thet I can. Anyways," Lloyd continued, "this feller, Lloyd Magruder, he was a man with a lot o' ambition and he and another feller started themselves a business in Elk City. Thet business was mainly a-takin' supplies into the back country fer the miners. You see, at thet period o' time, the gold rush was on and they was thousands o' fellers in the back country diggin' gold and livin' off the land. Right here in Newsome Creek, thar was thousands o' fellers livin' up and down the creek in tents."

Marty didn't comment on that, but he did look up and down the creek, as though he was visualizing thousands of tents, set up around the rock piles along Newsome Creek.

"There was a lot o' mining camps in these mountains in those days," Lloyd continued. "Mostly, there are no buildings or people where the old camps were, but in a few places, a small town kinda sprung up and folks still hang on there yet today. Places like Elk City, Dixie, Virginia City, Montana, and a few others are little communities. Places like Florence, Bufflar Hump, and the Gospels are gone. Only thing left in those places are the names and probably a bunch o' artifacts buried in the ground.

"Anyway, Magruder had a home in Lewiston, but he set himself up in business at Elk City, with this other feller. He had supplies brought in from Lewiston to his store in Elk City. From thet store, he would sell supplies to the local miners, but he would also run a pack string to the mining camps as far east as Virginia City. Virginia City o' course is now in Montana, but those days, all o' Idee-ho and Montana was considered Idaho or Washington territory. He would sell his supplies, get paid in gold, then bring the gold back across the Bitterroot Mountains to Elk City, then on to Lewiston."

"On the last trip Magruder made, he had five men with him. He hired on a couple more when he was over to Virginia City, Montana, and they turned out to be the bandits. Part o' the Henry Plummer gang, most folks believed."

"Who was Henry Plummer?" Marty wanted to know.

"He was sheriff over to Virginia City. Had hisself quite an operation. He knew who had gold and when and where they would take it. He had about twenty men, bandits, working fer him. He would jest send his men out and rob different miners when he found out they had a little gold. Most o' the robberies happened on the Old Nez Perce Indian Trail, 'cause it wound its way through the Bitterroot Mountains and they was no towns around or any place where there was a bunch o' people to catch the bandits. When the miners reported the robberies to Sheriff Plummer, he would always take a posse after the outlaws, but never did catch anyone. Usually the posse was made up o' outlaws and they would jest go out and meet up with the outlaws thet did the robbin', and all o' 'em would divvy up the gold. Quite an operation old Plummer had, but one day, a bunch o' fellers, who called themselves the Vigilantes, hung Sheriff Plummer and most o' his men. The robberies stopped directly."

"Did they hang him for killing Magruder?" Marty asked.

"Nope. They hung Plummer fer other robberies. There was never direct evidence thet Plummer was responsible for the Magruder murders, 'cept his association with the men thet did the killin'. Some folks say old Plummer was hung by the neck fore Magruder was kilt.

"Anyway, Magruder and his men, including the bandits,

left Bannack City in September 1863. They were carryin' thousands o' dollars in gold, both Magruder's and the miners' thet trusted their gold to Magruder.

"The bandits waited 'till they got sixty or seventy miles or so from Bannack, then they made their move. The bandits took them at night, when everyone was asleep, 'cept Magruder hisself. According to one o' the bandits, who later confessed, the bandit named Lower hit Magruder in the back o' the head with an axe, while he was bent over the campfire lightin' his pipe.

"They kilt three others o' the Magruder party with axes, too. They shot Magruder's top packer in the head, while he was asleep. I believe they called thet feller Charles Allen.

"One o' Magruder's men got his six-shooter out, but they got him with an axe before he did much shootin'. Anyway, they robbed all the bodies, chopped them up somewhat, and rolled them over a cliff."

"How come they chopped them up?" Marty asked, his face contorted in such a manner that reminded Lloyd of someone taking a bit from a fresh lemon.

"Wanted to make it look like Indians did the killin', I guess," Lloyd said. He continued with the story as Marty stared into the campfire.

"After they robbed the bodies o' the gold and personal effects, they built a big fire and burned all the saddles, harnesses, and everythin' else they didn't need, 'cept a few guns and cookin' items. Thet they hid. Magruder's friends found these things thet next spring."

"Did they find Magruder's gold?" Marty asked.

"Some was found on the bandits when they caught them, but most folks believe thet the outlaws hid the biggest share somewhere along the Nez Perce Indian Trail, back in the Bitterroot Mountains."

"How come people think the bandits hid the gold,

Grandpa? I would have taken it with me, if I was them."

"Well, ye got to figger, Boy, they had jest kilt five people. They wanted to get a long ways away, then come back in a year or so, get the gold, and live happy ever after.

"The reason folks think they may have hid the gold is fer a couple o' reasons. One, Magruder had 120 mules. There was rumor thet he had those mules loaded with other miners' gold ore. The outlaws killed the mules all along the trail from where the murders took place, clear out to the Camas Prairie. Folks got to thinkin' thet they would bury a little gold every so often, then kill the mules thet was a carryin' it. In this way, they could get the gold out o' the mountains toward Elk City and have all the stock out o' the way by the time they got to Elk City. They didn't want anyone to recognize Magruder's stock, 'cause he was well known in Elk City.

"Anyway, when the outlaws got to Lewiston, a feller who was a friend o' Magruder's, saw the outlaws with some o' Magruder's horses and his rifle. His friend started a-thinkin' and then started his own snoopin' around. Guess he talked with other fellers that saw Magruder leave Bannack City with his pack train and others that saw these fellers near Elk City with Magruder's stock. Anyway, he brought them in fer trial at Lewiston. They hung those fellers in the spring o' 1864 there in Lewiston.

"That is, they hung three o' them. One o' the men said he'd tell what happened, if'n they would let him go. They did, but he was kilt a couple years later, without ever tellen' anyone where the gold was hiddin', if in fact he knew."

"Wow!" Marty said. He was in awe. "What happened to the gold they did find?"

"I'm not sure," Lloyd replied. "I've been mostly interested in the gold they DIDN'T find."

"Did you look for it, Grandpa?" Marty asked.

Lloyd looked at his grandson for several moments, then

said. "Marty—" Lloyd only called him that when he was very serious about something. "I'm going to tell you something that you must not tell anyone. Promise!"

"I promise, Grandpa. What is it?"

Lloyd studied Marty's face a few minutes longer, then said, "I've been looking fer thet gold fer forty years. I haven't told a soul thet I have been, but a time or two, I've suspected others thet I met was doin' the same thing. I've rode the trail from where Magruder was kilt, clear back out to the Camas Prairie. I don't figure the outlaws hid the gold once they got to the prairie, 'cause it's open and more folks was around. I think the outlaws didn't want to attract a whole lotta attention, so they kilt all the mules before they got to the Prairie. Least ways, that's how the story goes. If'n it happened thet way, then the gold's got to be buried or hid in some way, along the trail in the mountains, 'cause they would have no way a packin' thet much gold without horses or mules. Course, I could be wrong, but Hill Beachy and the others from Lewiston found the dead mules all along the trail in different spots. But, who knows if they counted the mules or not? Maybe the outlaws kept ten or so o' the mules and packed the biggest share o' the gold a few miles off the trail. After all, they knew the trail was used by thousands o' miners and freighters, going to and from the gold fields, and they wouldn't want to chance someone else a-findin' thar gold."

"How do you know that Mr. Magruder had all that gold, Grandpa? Maybe the gold they found on the outlaws was all of the gold that Magruder had," Marty said.

Lloyd looked at his grandson thoughtfully. "You'll keep quiet 'bout what I'm fixin' to tell you, right?" Lloyd asked. Marty nodded.

"Well then, I'll tell ye," Lloyd said. "Most folks think there was more gold. I suppose rumors, and what not, started and jest got bigger as the years went by. Although, there is basis fer the rumors in this case. Probably one, or maybe several, miners told their kin that all their gold was stolen from Magruder when he was kilt, so the legend was just passed on down through the years. 'Cept in this case, it ain't jest a legend, it's a fact. You see Lloyd Magruder was a-haulin' over a quarter million dollars in gold ore, fer three different miners thet had struck it big. He was a-packin' his own gold too a course, but thet was dust and nuggets thet he'd been paid fer his supplies. Thet amounted to thirty thousand dollars or a little more, maybe."

Marty's eyes were wide and his mouth open as Lloyd continued. "Before Magruder left Bannack City, he wrote a letter to his wife in Lewiston. In the letter, he tells her thet he's got his own gold besides these other fellers' gold. He explained to his wife that he was a-takin' the gold out o' Bannack City fer these miner friends, 'cause the outlaws was a-robbin' and murderin' folks. I guess the miners had been hidin' thar gold fer fear the desperadoes would kill them fer it.

"Anyways, Magruder's letter didn't get to his wife in Lewiston. Whoever Magruder gave it to delivered it to someone in Elk City and thar it stayed until several months after his death.

"A feller by the name o' John Wick was Magruder's partner. Guess he was a-runnin' the store in Elk City fer Magruder. I suppose he somehow read the letter, 'cause he looked fer the gold a year or so after that or so they say."

"Did he ever find it, Grandpa?" Marty asked.

"Nope, he never did. Neither did the others and neither did I, and I been looking fer it off and on now fer over forty years. I was twenty-one when I started a lookin'."

"Maybe there is no gold, Grandpa. Maybe Magruder

never sent no letter. Maybe that Mr. Wick was tellin' a whopper, Grandpa," Marty said, almost yelling in disbelief, but eager for the story to go on.

"Letter is real enough," Lloyd said. "I read it with my very own eyes. A daughter o' Magruder's friend, Lucy Maxwell, ended up with it. She showed it to me years ago, up to Elk City, whar she lives."

"What did the letter say, Grandpa?" Marty asked.

"Don't remember the particulars, but I do remember the part about all thet gold he was a-carryin'. Seems to me he was a mite concerned 'bout a-carryin' it too. Maybe I should go back and re-read Lucy's letter, might find more information thet would be helpful.

"I do remember Lucy a-tellin' me thet her mother, Sarah, seen the bones o' those mules. Said she rode over the trail with her daddy, when he was a-lookin' fer the gold. Said he pointed out the mules' bones to her, and her mother remembers most o' the skeletons being in one general location, 'bout four or five miles from where Magruder was kilt.

"If'n thet be the case, I'd say those bandits probably hid most o' the gold right around where they kilt everyone, or maybe they packed it aways on the mules, then hid it. Course, if thet was the case, then the outlaw, Page, would have probably told whar the gold was, seein's he told 'bout everything else when he confessed."

"Page was the name of one of the outlaws?" Marty asked.

"Yes, Renton, Romaine, and Lower were the other three, and like I already told you, they were hanged in Lewiston," Lloyd said.

"I wonder what Magruder and the other men were like?" Marty asked, almost thoughtfully, as he stared into the campfire, which Lloyd added more wood to.

"Don't know much about the other fellers with Magruder, but I did learn a mite 'bout Magruder hisself, during the

30

time I was a-lookin' fer his gold," Lloyd said.

"What did you learn about Magruder, Grandpa?" Marty asked.

"Well, I found out thet Magruder was a persistent, ambitious feller. He originally came from Montgomery County, Maryland. He was one o' thirteen children. I hear tell he was an orphan at age eleven. Thet's 'bout yer age, ain't it, boy?" Lloyd asked.

"Nope," Marty quickly replied. "I'm thirteen today, Grandpa, remember my birthday."

Lloyd's eyes twinkled as he smiled. "Oh, guess thet's right, Boy, ye are older 'n eleven, ain't ye.

"Anyway," Lloyd continued, "Magruder joined up with the Army to fight the Mexicans in 1846. He married a gal by the name o' Caroline in 1847, and after the war with Mexico, Magruder moved to Californy. Magruder tried his hand at several things in Californy, tried a little lawyering, surveying, mining, and even tried to be a politician and a store merchant. Anyway, things jest never seemed to work out fer Magruder. He would start to be successful, then somethin' would happen and jest knock him back down agin.

"Well, in 1860, the Gold Rush started here in these parts. I guess Old Magruder heerd 'bout it, 'cause he came to Ideeho in 1862, and in jest a few months, he had a store opened in Elk City, with another. I think thet feller's name was John Wick and he run it. They say Wick hunted fer the gold, but never found it, then he jest disappeared into time."

Marty shook his head that he understood, even though he was deep in thought.

"Anyways," Lloyd continued, "you know the rest o' the story. One o' these here times, I'll show ye all the places I've looked fer the gold and all the places I ain't looked. Maybe one o' these days we'll get lucky and rich."

Marty passed the rest of the afternoon fishing, or at least

going through the motions of fishing. He didn't really fish, he didn't even see George Timick break camp and leave in his car. His mind was searching for answers about the hidden gold and the murders of the Magruder Party.

Marty went to sleep early that night and dreamed. He dreamed dreams that he would remember for the rest of his life. Just before he woke up at 6:00 A.M., Marty saw a man slip from the bushes and conceal himself behind a large pine tree near their camp. He couldn't see the man's features, but he could see that he was carrying an axe. In a few moments, he saw three more men creep from behind the bushes.

They didn't conceal themselves, but simply walked toward him. He couldn't see their faces, but all were holding axes. The man behind the tree stepped forth with his axe. Marty could now see his face. It was George Timick and he was smiling.

3

The Dream

Wednesday, July 15, 1863

The North—The New York riots are finally quelled by armed troops. The majority of the 1,000 slain, die at the hands of the Army, that fires rifles into the mob. The Irish community is outraged at the government and opposition to the draft increases.

Eastern Theater—The Army of Northern Virginia withdraws along the Shenandoah Valley. Meade finally orders his men forward, only to find that the Confederate positions around Williamsport are held by a small rear guard. The Federals overrun it and capture some wounded and a few stragglers.

Brigadier General James Pettigrew, whose brigade had opened the battle of Gettysburg, is killed in this last skirmish of the campaign.

Lincoln is furious at Meade for allowing the beaten Confederates to escape so easily. "We had them within our grasp," he complains. "We had only to stretch forth our hands and they were ours."

Western Theater—Morgan reaches the bank of the Ohio near Buffington Bar, during the evening.

Federal troops are closing in on his tiring troops. Within a few hours, Morgan's brigade is cut to pieces by superior

Union forces. Some one hundred twenty of the raiders are killed and seven hundred captured. Morgan himself escapes with three hundred raiders. Reaching the West Virginia shore, he then heads north for Pennsylvania.

Far West—Since the defeat of the Sioux Indians in Minnesota during the fall of 1862, the most implacable Indian bands have retreated to the Dakota Territory. The forces pursuing them intercept a large group of Sioux near what will later become Bismarck, North Dakota. The First Minnesota Mounted Rangers, three volunteer infantry regiments and an artillery battery, are engaged all day. The Indian losses are heavy.

Hill Beachy sat up in his bed with a start. He was soaked with his perspiration. For a moment, he didn't know where he was, but slowly he recognized the log walls and canvas top of his Luna House Hotel.

Hill swung his feet off the bed and rubbed them across the rough board floor. "Damn! What kind of dream . . . ? Damn, that was so real . . . felt like I was there. Gotta tell Lloyd, gotta warn him. That must of been some kinda warning to be so real."

"What's real?" Margaret Beachy asked her husband as she came through the bedroom door, carrying a cup of hot coffee and a plate of scrambled eggs and toast.

Hill looked at his wife, rubbed his face, and said, "Dream, Margaret. I had a dream about Lloyd getting killed. It was real, almost like I was right there watching, only I couldn't do anything about it. Some men in his night camp used axes and killed him and took his gold and personal possessions."

"Dreams are just dreams, darling." Margaret Beachy said, as she set Hill's plate of eggs on the night stand. She handed him his coffee, then rubbed his receding hairline.

"Don't rub too hard, honey," Hill said. "Those head hairs come out easy now. I must be getting old."

"Thirty-five is not old," Margaret replied, "and I don't care if you lose every one of them. You are still my Hilly." She bent down and kissed his forehead. "You better get dressed. Remember Clay Thompson is bringing a wagon load of boards for the roof over."

"Oh, yah, I forgot about that," Hill said as he glanced up at the canvas roof of his Luna House Hotel. "I want to go see Lloyd first. I need to warn him that he better forget going into the Wilderness. I know that what I saw wasn't just a dream. It was like a visual premonition that is actually going to happen."

"Some dreams are very real, dear," Margaret replied. "But, don't tell Lloyd, honey. It is just a dream and you know Lloyd. He tells Caroline everything, and she's already worried sick about Lloyd's trip. He's going to be gone three months, and if she hears about your dream, well, I'm not sure she can handle it."

Hill thought about that. He knew Caroline and, damn, Margaret was right. Caroline just might become ill if she knew about his dream.

"All right," Hill said. "I won't tell him, but I am going to try and talk him out of going. I mean, after all, he has been nominated as Territorial Delegate to Congress for the new Idaho Territory. Lewiston is the capital and Lloyd's needed here, not running around the wilderness."

"Do you think he will listen?" Margaret asked.

"Who knows?" Hill replied. "Lloyd Magruder is a stubborn, persistent man when he's got his mind made up. I am going to try, though," Hill said, as he slipped on his trousers and boots.

Hill Beachy wasn't a man who saw ghosts. He didn't believe in premonitions or unexplained phenomena, but he did believe in what his eyes saw. In his mind, he saw Lloyd Magruder murdered in the wilderness.

Hill Beachy was a man who believed in his own abilities to accomplish things. Action was the key to Hill's success. When he was thirteen, he left home and took a job as a cabin boy working the steamboats on the Mississippi River. There, he learned the art of baking and when the Mexican War broke out, he put his trade to use and started a bakery on the Rio Grande, selling bread to the soldiers. It was here that Hill met Lloyd and they became friends.

After the war, Hill returned to the steamboat and eventually became a pilot.

In 1849, Hill left the steamboats and tried his hand at mining, with his friend Lloyd. They worked the mines around San Francisco, Sacramento, and Marysville, but had no real success. Hill met his wife, Margaret Anne Early, in Marysville and shortly after their wedding, the couple moved to Red Bluff, California. Never idle, Hill and Margaret started a hotel under the name of the Luna House.

In the spring of 1862, Hill and Margaret sold out and moved to Idaho, following the opportunities provided by the new gold fields. Hill settled in Lewiston, where he ran into his old friend, Lloyd Magruder. With Lloyd's encouragement, Hill started his second Luna House Hotel.

Although Lloyd didn't have a lot of extra cash, he had loaned Hill five hundred dollars to get the Luna House in operation. Hill liked Lloyd. Lloyd was a man of action, but even more, Lloyd was honest and kind. He was a man whom you could trust. A man who could help lead this new wilderness territory and a man who should have his friends stand by him. Hill intended to do just that.

It took Hill about a half hour to find Lloyd and when he did, it was on the new steamboat, *Lewiston,* docked at the confluence of the Snake and Clearwater rivers. Lloyd was conducting inventory of his supplies that the *Lewiston* had brought in the night before.

"Makin' ready to head for the wild, are you?" Hill asked, as he approached Lloyd in the cargo bay of the *Lewiston*.

Lloyd smiled as he turned and saw his friend. "Hill! How are you?" Lloyd asked with genuine interest.

"Oh, just fine, Lloyd," Hill replied. "I guess I missed you when I got back from Nevada."

"Yah, I was in Portland putting this miner's supply package together," Lloyd said. "You know, Hill, this will be the biggest supply train ever to reach the miners in the wilderness. With this merchandise, and what I've already got at the store in Elk City, I should clear over thirty thousand dollars, if I can sell everything, and I know I can," Lloyd said. Hill winced, but said nothing at first.

"This trip will do for me what I've been trying to do for years," Lloyd said. "I will be able to buy Caroline the home she's always wanted and now, maybe, I can finally settle down and quit moving all over the country."

"That's kinda what I wanted to talk to you about, Lloyd." Settling down, Hill said, "Lloyd, why don't you give up this idea of going into the wilderness with these supplies? You know that your nomination as delegate to Congress will go through, Lloyd. You know that you really should stay here in Lewiston and get all the people behind you. Let people get to know you, Lloyd, and you'll go a long way. Let Allen and Phillips take the train into the wilderness. Why take unnecessary risk, Lloyd?"

Lloyd stood looking at his friend. He was a little confused. Hill Beachy had never talked like that before. Hill Beachy wasn't the kind of man to let others handle a business when it was his to handle.

"Hill, I-I'm kinda surprised," Lloyd stammered. "You don't really think Allen and Phillips could do what needs to be done on this business venture, do you?" Lloyd asked.

Hill blushed, he knew Lloyd was right. He knew that Allen and Phillips could not handle this undertaking. Both were good, honest, and reliable men, but neither had ventured beyond mining, trapping, and a lot of mule skinning.

"Well, I was just thinking of all the desperadoes and drifters around the country now days, Lloyd. You know of all the reports of miners being robbed and killed in the camps?"

"Yah, I've heard," Lloyd said, "but, I've also heard that the vigilantes hung a bunch of those toughs over in Virginia City, including that Sheriff Plummer, who was their leader."

"That's true, Lloyd, but there are still some bad ones out there. Hell, Lloyd, everyone in Lewiston knows you're taking a fortune in merchandise into the wilderness. You'll be a sitting duck for any tough with an itchy trigger finger and a thirst for some easy money."

"Look, Hill," Lloyd said, "I appreciate your concern, but I've got to make this trip. You are right when you say I've got to let the people know me. That's what part of this trip is all about. There are thousands of miners back in those mountains and when the right time comes, they'll vote for me because they know that I'm one of them. I don't want people to vote for me like most politicians draw votes. I don't want to sit back and make promises and blow a bunch of hot air. I want to be a representative of the people, because, by God, I care and because I can do the job. I want to learn what this new territory is all about and I want to be here as it grows. I'm already here, at its birth, and I find it beautiful, exciting, and untamed, ready for direction. Don't you see, Hill, I've got to make this trip for myself. I'm tired of failing. I don't want any more Marysville, San Francisco, or Sacramento failures. I got to those places too late, but I'm here on time and I've got the education and experience to make it with this opportunity."

Hill nodded his head, he knew Lloyd was right. He just hoped it wouldn't cost Lloyd his life to be right.

"Okay," Hill said. "How about you and Caroline coming over to dinner tonight? We can at least spend a little time together before you take off."

Lloyd grinned. "Sure, but promise not to try and talk me into staying here. Caroline doesn't need any help."

"Promise," Hill said, wondering if he should confide in Caroline, even if it meant breaking Lloyd's confidence. Hill waved his good-bye as Lloyd turned back to his inventory. "Supper's at six," he yelled back into the cargo bay, as he left the *Lewiston.*

4

The Gifts

Saturday, July 23, 1863

Eastern Theater—Infantry formed the bulk of both armies and the Union alone was able to raise 1,666 infantry regiments, plus over 300 independent infantry companies.

This vast number of troops had as its main weapon, the rifle, which appeared in many forms and varying numbers. The Union government establishments could not handle all the work and many private firms were used. The 1861 Model U.S. Percussion Rifle Musket totaled over 700,000 weapons alone. Specialist single-shot rifles were also produced in large numbers, as the war ground on, with a consequent increase in type and variety.

Far West—Large pro-Union demonstrations take place in San Francisco, California.

"Is Lloyd still insistent on making this wilderness trip, Caroline?" Margaret asked, while they were studying the Luna House's new roof, just recently constructed by Clay Thompson.

"I'm afraid so," Caroline replied. "That's all he ever talks about anymore, unless it's the war. He sympathizes with the South, of course, and if he wasn't set on this wilderness trip, he would be right back there in the middle of it. He lost his brother at Gettysburg, you know?"

"Oh! No, I didn't, Caroline," Margaret said. "I'm sorry. Hill didn't mention anything to me about it."

"Lloyd probably didn't tell Hill about it," Caroline said. "He keeps all of his emotions inside. He won't even tell me how he feels, and I know he's just dying inside. Sometimes, though, he does write about his feelings. I saw tears in his eyes when he read the letter from his mother about his brother, Elda.

"I love that man so much, but he won't talk or open up to me . . ." Caroline stopped and put her hand across her mouth. Margaret could see tears in her eyes.

"If he fails one more time, I don't see how he will ever be able to take it," she continued. "I don't know if I'll be able to take it. If it's not the wilderness, it's the war. I don't know which is the worst, wilderness, war, or failure."

"He won't fail, Caroline," Margaret said, as she hugged her. "He won't go back to that awful war either. Lloyd will make his fortune in the wilderness, and both of you and the children will be happy. I mean, look at his success already, Caroline. He just had a new home built. I understand that he's made enough from the store in Elk City to purchase more mules. Things will be okay."

"I suppose you are right," Caroline said, as she used her handkerchief to dab at the tears in her eyes. "I just had this awful feeling that things aren't going to be all right."

Margaret looked at Caroline. She didn't tell Caroline, but she, too, had a bad feeling about Lloyd. Maybe it was Hill's dream or maybe a combination of Caroline's emotions and the dream. She didn't know and she didn't like it.

"Let's talk about something else, Caroline. Lloyd's store in Elk City, he has a new partner running it, doesn't he?" Margaret asked.

"Yes, but I don't really know him," Caroline said. "Lloyd

41

said he knew the man and even worked for him as a surveyor for mining claims when we lived in Marysville. He's nice enough," she continued, "but, he does seem to be a little greedy. Lloyd says that's just his business sense at work. Lloyd thinks he's a smart man and I'm sure he is, but he doesn't look the type to run a store in the rugged wilderness of Idaho Territory. Lloyd say's that things will work, though, because Charles Allen and Bill Phillips will take care of the supplies and getting them to Elk City, while Mr. Wick handles the selling. Brain work, as Lloyd calls it."

"Mr. Wick, is that Lloyd's partner's name?" Margaret asked.

"Ladies, could you join us down here?" Hill yelled up the stairs. "We're in the study, honey," he said.

Margaret smiled as she and Caroline started down the stairs to the main floor of the Luna House.

"Study," she said and she giggled. "It's just a guest room that he uses for his office, study, or storage, whatever the situation may be. My guess is Hill wants to make some kind of speech, if he's calling it his study."

Both women laughed and went on downstairs. In the study Hill stood smiling, holding a log box about four and a half feet tall and eight inches wide.

"I want to make my friend a presentation," Hill said. "I want his wife and mine," he smiled and looked at Margaret, "present when I do so."

The women looked at Lloyd, who was standing a little awkwardly, near the door, with a look of amusement and maybe a little embarrassment mixed in.

"I've known Lloyd for better than eight years now, and I consider him my very best friend. In light of that friendship and Lloyd's soon-to-be trip into the wilderness, I want to present him with this present."

Hill handed Lloyd the box. Lloyd looked at the women, then back at Hill. "Hill, you shouldn't have . . . you don't have to give me anything."

"Just open it, Lloyd," Hill said sharply.

Lloyd looked around again, this time in embarrassment over the emotion and affection his friend was displaying.

Lloyd looked at the box, then reached into his pocked for a small knife. He pried the box apart and gasped at what it held.

"Right from Mr. Morse himself." Hill smiled brightly. "I ordered it three months ago, haven't even seen it myself until today," Hill said. "Came in on the *Lewiston* today with your supplies. See, it even has a plate on the bottom of the stock. Let me read it," Hill said, as he gently took the rifle from Lloyd.

The plate read "Rifle of Hill Beachy, Model 1854, .44 cal. Morse Repeater."

Lloyd stood with his mouth open, looking at Hill. It was several moments before he could talk. "Well, do you like it?" Hill asked. "It's the newest firearm in existence today. Shoots fifteen times without reloading. You use the lever on the bottom to reload after each shot."

"Gosh, Hill. I . . . I can't take your rifle. It's even got your name plate on it."

"I know that," Hill said, "and I want you to have it. Where you're going, you may need to kill quite a bit of your own food." Hill glanced at Caroline to see if she was guessing there might be another reason why he was giving her husband the finest rifle ever made. She didn't appear to notice any significance in the gift, so Hill suspected she didn't know much about firearms.

Lloyd didn't want to take his friend's rifle, but he knew he didn't have a choice. He knew this was Hill's way of saying that he cared and really believed there was danger ahead for him.

Lloyd thanked Hill several times, as he marveled and examined the weapon. With this and his Navy 6, Lloyd could sustain a rate of fire never before equalled by any one man. Lloyd couldn't imagine a rifle that shot fifteen times without reloading. He had never even heard of such a weapon.

"Hill, I don't know what to say," Lloyd finally said.

"Just say thanks," Hill said, enjoying his friend's appreciation of the gift.

"Where. . . . How did a gun like this get invented, Hill?" Lloyd asked.

"A man by the name of Samuel Finley Breese Morse invented it in 1854. It shoots cartridges, metallic cases full of powder. Morse tried to sell it to the U.S. Army soon after he manufactured fifteen or twenty of them, but they wouldn't even consider it. They said the rifle was too extravagant and dangerous for military use.

"Morse sold a few to private owners, but they never seemed to make it out on the market. I got this one, and one other, from a friend of mine in San Francisco. My friend is Thomas Morse, Samuel's son. We were partners for a short time in some mines around Marysville. That was probably about three years before I met you, I guess," Hill said.

Lloyd worked the rifle lever and wondered at its workmanship and amazing action in chambering rounds.

"I have something for you as well, Lloyd." Lloyd looked at Caroline as she spoke. She was smiling and holding a small leather sack. Hill and Margaret were also smiling and watching Lloyd, as Caroline placed the sack in Lloyd's hand. Lloyd stood the rifle in a corner and opened the sack. Reaching inside, he pulled out a beautiful silver pocket watch, with a chain. His initials, "L.M.," were engraved on top of the closed lid. Opening it, he saw a tiny photograph of Caroline, which she had taken in Portland nearly a year ago.

Lloyd swallowed hard. He was nearly overwhelmed by the love of his wife and friends. Lloyd stepped to the three of them and embraced them all together. A tiny tear started at the corner of his eye, but he quickly wiped it away with a finger.

5

The Partner

John Wick was a smart man. He was also a very greedy man, and just now, he was an angry greedy man. He stared at the crumpled letter from his attorney, which he had just thrown to the floor.

What else could go wrong? He thought. *Why the hell should I sit up here in the middle of this wilderness, in this dreary remote community, and get fifteen percent of profits? I'm the one doing all the work, suffering all boredom, and putting up with these stupid people.*

Now my wife leaves and takes with her the $7,000 I had saved up. To make matters worse, she runs off with some bastard who was probably waiting for me to leave, he thought.

Wick reached down and retrieved the crumpled letter from the floor. He straightened the letter back out and reread it just to be sure he hadn't missed anything or misread it in anyway.

He read the letter aloud to himself. It read and was addressed as follows.

Mr. John Wick
Magruder & Wick Mining Supplies
Elk City, Idaho Territory

Dear Mr. Wick,
    I am very sorry to inform you that your now estranged

wife has departed the Marysville area and has taken with her the $7,000 from the Marysville Bank that you had on deposit of trust to our joint account. You may ask how she was able to get the funds without my signature or yours, since her name was not on the account.

I have taken the liberty to conduct an inquiry and have learned the following, which I believe explains how she managed to extract those funds.

It seems that after your departure from Marysville, in April of 1862, Mrs. Wick started to work at a bakery, the business name, I believe was referred to as "The Maple Shop."

At any rate, it seems she took up with a co-worker, a good-looking young man, who went by the name of Buck Welch. It seems that Mr. Welch had recently been let out of prison for forgery. Word is, he spent two years In Yuma for this crime. He also bragged that he was very good at this type of thing.

The next matter that I need to inform you of is very distressful and I am very uncomfortable in doing so, but do so I must.

While making our inquiry, my man learned that your wife, Janet, if I may refer to her with her given name, had been making frequent trips to a Doctor Ronald Higgins's office, here in Marysville. From Dr. Higgins's nurse, we learned that your Janet was pregnant and that Mr. Welch was believed to be the father.

Shortly after her last visit to Dr. Higgins's office, both she and Mr. Welch quit their jobs at the bakery and that very afternoon, Janet withdrew the funds from the bank, on a letter of authority, signed by you and me. The bank currently holds this letter.

Needless to say, I have contacted the authorities, but as of the writing of this letter, I have heard nothing. We have heard that Mrs. Wick and her friend may be traveling to San Francisco, California, where, according to one of her friends, she will have her baby.

If you have any instructions for me, please forward same with haste.

Sincerely and in Your Service,
John B. Teal
Attorney At Law

John Wick trembled as he finished reading the letter. If Janet were before him at this very moment, he would shoot her. Wick tried to examine his feelings. He didn't care about Janet's affair. *Good-bye and good riddance,* he thought. He hadn't planned on going back to Janet anyway. The only reason he married her in the first place was to get close to her father's money, or what he though was money. As it turned out, the old man had very little money and what little he did have went for funeral expenses. After the other bills were all paid, Janet was able to claim one hundred thirty-two dollars and fifty-two cents.

Not much, he thought, but it had topped off his account at seven thousand dollars. *Now, that bitch took it all.* Here he was in the wilderness, nearly penniless, working for little more than meager wages. "For what!" he said aloud.

Wick's anger at his unfaithful wife was suddenly channeled toward the senior partner in the store, Lloyd Magruder. John Wick had had a resentment against Lloyd almost from the day they formed the partnership. Lloyd and Wick had run into each other at an auction in Portland. Having been acquainted in Marysville, the two had struck up a conversation, which had led to a dinner together that evening.

Lloyd had brought along Caroline, which had angered Wick. He had little use for women, except when he had certain needs. Wick was disgusted with Lloyd for taking Caroline with him to the wilderness. Women were a bother and interfered with business. If he had had his way, he would have sent Caroline packing, but that damn Magruder had the controlling interest in the business.

In fact, had it not been for Lloyd's generous offer, Wick would not have had fifteen percent in the business. Being nearly broke, Wick had accepted Magruder's offer to run the Elk City store for fifteen percent of net profit. Lloyd was to purchase all supplies and build the store with his money. With Lloyd on the trail ninety percent of the time, Wick would be able to skim maybe another fifteen or twenty percent and before long, he might even have his own business, if he could figure a way to take the trade from Magruder. He knew he could, it had worked before in Marysville. Now, all of that was lost.

All because of a lying, cheating, thieving woman. Wick wished he had beat her harder. He should have broken her before he left. Actually, he thought he had broken her. He figured she would have been too afraid of him to leave, let alone take all of his money when she did leave. *It must have been that bastard she ran off with,* he thought. "It must have been him that put the idea in her head. She was too stupid to think of that by herself. Damn!" he shouted and banged his fist down hard on the desk.

If it hadn't been for Magruder, he wouldn't have taken this stupid job in the middle of nowhere, and he would still have his seven thousand dollars. Wick rubbed his receding hairline, then smashed his fist down on the desk again. The impact knocked over his open ink well, spilling ink over the business books and other business papers. This sent Wick into a rage.

Grabbing the underside of the desk, he heaved upward, turning the desk over almost before it hit the floor on its side. He then began kicking the desk violently. The roll top cover and one side panel of the desk were destroyed before he was able to regain his composure. Breathing heavily, Wick climbed the stairs to his living quarters. There, he went to his bed and reached under. He dragged a two-foot by two-foot long wooden box out. The box was locked with a padlock, which he unlocked with a key that was attached to his pocket watch chain. Reaching inside, Wick pulled out a two-inch thick diary. Many men drank to deal with their anger. Wick liked to put his on paper, so he could see it. He loved his anger—he loved his strategy to deal with things that annoyed him—loved to put it before his eyes in writing, so he could destroy it. Only then could he calm down, only then would the rage subside.

Wick frantically flipped through the pages, trying to find some of the entries that angered and satisfied him the most. Finally he stopped and read.

June 2nd, 1861—Marysville
Janet asked for some money today, said she wanted to buy some "personal" things that women need. I told her such things were not worth spending money on. She started to cry, so I slapped her across the face. She really hollered then, so I kicked her in the ass. Had to kick her several times before she shut up.
At least she now knows who's boss and when I tell her something, she knows I mean it.

He then continued flipping pages, but stopped again when he came to the date:

July 3rd, 1862—Portland
I met Lloyd Magruder at the Vancouver Hotel today. He bought me dinner and offered me 15% interest in a business that he is starting in the new territory gold camps. I felt this was rather a low percent, for I employed Magruder as a surveyor in the mine camps around Marysville back in 60–61.
You would think he would have been more appreciative. I'm sure he would have taken my offer of 25%, if his nosy wife would have kept her trap shut. I remember her words. I'm sorry

50

Mr. Wick, we can only pay 15% at this time. Our initial capital outlay has been too great to pay you anything other than 15%.

Wick remembered her sickening smile when she finished talking. He also remembered how he visualized back handing her out of her chair and telling the bitch to shut up. He didn't, of course, but oh, how he had wanted to. Women had always caused him to fail and consequently, evoked his anger. Women had always told him what to do or undermined him. Always he either failed in what he was attempting, or got hurt for his efforts.

When he was a kid in New York, "that whore of a mother" was always telling him to "get out." Four, five, six times a day, even in the winter, he would have to leave the house while some Atlantic seaman rutted around on her. He could remember the bitch grunting and moaning, while the drunken sailors sometimes stood in line waiting for her.

Wick remembered one sailor asking him, "Hey, kid. You got a sister stashed around here someplace? It's getting too cold to wait for yer ol' lady." They had all laughed then, some of them even falling to the ground and rolling in the snow with laughter. That was the day he left. That was the day the sailors had jerked his mother naked from the house. That was the day they all had a go at her in the snow. Her screams were real then, but he was glad. She deserved everything they gave her.

That was the day fifteen-year-old John Wick quit feeling pain and started giving it. That was fifteen years ago.

6

Romain and Renton

Sunday, August 2, 1863

Western Theater—Sherman continues his efforts to isolate Confederate General Hood in Atlanta. Hood has not been able to fathom Sherman's plan, neither has he realized that Sherman knows his every step. He doesn't realize that because of this knowledge, Generals Thomas and Howard cut the rail line from Atlanta to Montgomery, leaving the line to Macon as Atlanta's only lifeline.

Hood sends two corps under Hardee and Lee to take up positions at Jonesboro, on the Macon line. He does not realize that the Federal Armies of Thomas, Howard, and Schofield are already within striking distance and are concentrating to finally isolate Atlanta. Hood has no idea that his every plan has been monitored by Union spies.

Margaret didn't like the looks of the two men. Both were tall and unshaven. It looked like they had been in the saddle for a long time.

They weren't very friendly when they asked for a room, but Margaret supposed that was a matter of choice. She hadn't seen the men since they had checked in at ten this morning and requested a bath at one o'clock in the afternoon. It seemed strange to her that rugged men like that would make an appointment to take a bath. After all, she did have bath water heated all day every day.

Margaret guessed that it didn't matter, though. She had six tubs in two different bath houses at the back of the Luna House. Come to think of it, she thought Lloyd and his two packers were coming in at one for their baths. She was suddenly glad for the two bath houses. She wouldn't want to put Lloyd and his friends in with a pair of toughs like those two.

Just then Hill walked in. He had been down at the river helping Lloyd take his supplies from the *Lewiston,* while Bill Phillips and Chuck Allen packed everything on mules. "Hi, honey," he said. "What's for lunch?"

"I've got fried pork chops and potatoes on the stove ready to eat, dear," Margaret replied.

Hill went directly to the stove and started filling a plate. He was ravaged. "Starting to work at 5:00 A.M. gets a man hungry," he said.

"Yes, dear," Margaret replied. "Gets a woman hungry, too."

Hill smiled, as he finished filling his plate and turned from the stove to the table. He kissed Margaret on the forehead before he sat down, then asked, "Well, any customers this morning?"

"Two," she replied. "Rough-looking men. They make me uneasy."

"Where they from?" Hill asked.

"I don't know. They didn't say anything, except that they wanted a room and a bath at one this afternoon."

Hill frowned. Something made him feel uneasy. "What's their names?" he asked.

Margaret got up, went to the lobby, and picked up the open register. "Well, they signed in as David Renton and James Romain."

Hill thought for a moment, but couldn't place either

name. "Did they say what they were doing or where they were going?" he asked.

"No, not a word. Just went straight to their rooms and haven't come out yet," Margaret said. "They are probably sleeping. They looked pretty trail weary."

Hill shrugged his shoulders and continued to eat. Most of the men who checked in there fit that description. Lewiston was a long ways from nowhere if you traveled south or east toward the gold fields and three hundred or more miles if you went west toward Portland or the coast. The only easy way of travel was this way, by one of the riverboats, down the Snake River to the Columbia, then on to the coast. Hill supposed they hadn't come from the west.

Hill dismissed the two men from his thoughts. There were a lot of toughs and desperate men in Lewiston and half of them stayed at the Luna House.

"Is Lloyd and his men leaving this afternoon, then?" Margaret asked.

"No," Hill replied, "but Bill and Charles are. They have sixty mules, so Lloyd wants to get started as soon as possible. Says he wants to be back here in Lewiston by the middle of October."

"Well, when is Lloyd going to leave?" Margaret asked.

"He will leave in the morning. He wants to spend one more day with Caroline and the kids. Won't be any problem. He can catch up with the supply train in half a day."

At the confluence boat house, Lloyd Magruder finished his new supply order and gave it to Captain Hank Cole of the *Lewiston*. "This order is larger than the one you just got," Cole remarked to Lloyd.

"Yea, I know, Hank, and the next one will be even larger. They've started a new gold field, you know. They call it Florence. By next spring there will probably be eight or nine thousand miners going in there."

"Things really starting to boom, are they?" Cole asked. "Maybe I should quit running riverboats and join you."

"Don't you dare." Lloyd grinned. "Men like you are the life blood of this community and the gold camps."

"You make a man feel mighty important," Cole said.

"You are. Not many men would have the skill to bring boars up this river."

"Heck," Cole said, "These rivers running to Portland ain't so bad. Before I come here, I used to run the Mississippi, nothing but hidden sandbars all over. Been more than one riverboat lost in that river. Of course, if you try and take a boat much above Lewiston here, then it gets real tricky. In fact, there's only been one man to take a paddle wheeler above Lewiston and that's Captain Leonard White. He's also the first pilot to bring a paddle wheeler to Lewiston. He did that in 1859. Quite a man, that one is," Cole said, with obvious admiration for his fellow seaman.

"Matter of fact, here comes the *Wright* now," Cole said. "That's White's boat. Gets paid $500 a month to pilot her, if that tells you anything."

Lloyd looked downstream and saw the *Wright* just entering the confluence of the Snake and Clearwater. Three long blasts from her horn echoed across the water. "She's coming in fast," Lloyd commented.

"That she is," Cole replied, "but White can handle her."

Lloyd and Hank watched the *Wright* for several minutes, as she maneuvered along the Lewiston side of the Snake and then shut her engines down, after river men had her secured fore and aft with eight-inch Hauser lines.

"Quite an operation," Lloyd mused aloud. He then changed the subject, when he remembered that he was trying to do business with Hank.

"Hank, I need a breakdown on your current freight prices, so I can budget this November order."

Hank handed Lloyd a price list.

Portland to The Dalles (121 Miles)	$15.00
Portland to Umatilla (217 Miles)	$45.00
Portland to Wallula (240 Miles)	$50.00
Portland to Lewiston (401 Miles)	$90.00

"All freight costs are figured by measurement," Hank said. "Forty cubic feet equalling one ton. Other words, those crated miners shovels you ordered measured a cubic ton and hold ninety shovels, a freight cost of ninety dollars a ton."

"Whew," said Lloyd and whistled. "Pretty steep, but then again not so steep when you figure the effort getting the freight to the gold camps. I just wish there was a cheaper way."

"Maybe in a hundred years or so," Cole said, "but not now."

"Guess you are right," Lloyd said. "Well, better get going, Hank. Thanks for your help and I'll see you in November."

"Okay, Lloyd, you take it easy and be careful in the back country."

"Will do," Lloyd replied, and walked down the boat house plankway to the riverbank.

Two men followed Lloyd at a discreet distance back to the Luna House, where Lloyd met Bill and Charles.

Margaret Beachy saw Romain and Renton enter the Luna House from the rear door. She thought it strange, because the front door faced Main Street. The only thing out the back door was a little-used path to the river.

Soon after Lloyd and his packers called for their bath water, Romain approached Margaret in the lobby and requested his and Renton's bath water. Margaret sent the house boy, John Lee, to do this task, while she talked with Clay Thompson about the construction of an additional bath house.

Other than Hill Beachy, Lloyd Magruder trusted no one more than he did Charles Allen and William Phillips. Both men had worked for him and both men had long since proved their honesty and reliability. That's why Lloyd told them about the gold while sitting in the Luna House bath. They knew they were going to be carrying Lloyd's gold and a little of their own back. But they hadn't known they would be carrying gold for three of the biggest and most profitable miners from Bannack City. Both men had wondered why Lloyd had had them purchase sixty head of mules last year under a false name and leave them at Elk City in the care of a miner, whom Lloyd said he had already paid and trusted. They now realized they would be bringing one hundred twenty mules on the return trip.

They lay in bed facing each other. Their love-making had been furious, yet very tender. Caroline loved Lloyd so much that she simply ached at the thought of him being gone for three days, let alone three months.

"Today is August second. By the latter part of October, I'll be back in Lewiston. I'll be back and I'll never have to leave you again."

Lloyd's assurance about not ever leaving her again was a very welcome relief, but it didn't help the misery that she was now starting to feel. "Oh, darling, do you really have to go?" she asked. "The children just won't understand. John Carter is only seven and he will ask me every day where you're at. Eliza will cry for a week. That's what they did the last time you went to Portland for supplies and business."

"I know, honey," Lloyd said. "But with this trip, I can achieve financial success and, very probably, political success. After this trip, any time I go anywhere, you and the kids can go with me.

"You know, after this trip," he said solemnly, "I could be

on the road to the governorship of Idaho Territory. The capital is right here, honey. We won't have to move. Hill and Margaret are here to stay and Lewiston is a great place to live."

"I know," she said, "but I just wish you were back safe. The wilderness and gold camps are so dangerous."

"Hey, are you forgetting the rifle that Hill gave me? Not to mention Charles Allen and William Phillips, neither of those boys are pilgrims."

"I know, dear. I'm just being a woman, you'll have to cope with that, I guess." She smiled, as did Lloyd. Lloyd thought her to be the most beautiful woman in the world. He kissed her on the nose, lips, and chin, as he slid his hand slowly up her stomach and cupped her full breast. He moved gently back on top of her and they made love again, slowly and tenderly for the last time in their lives.

It was 9:00 A.M. by the time Lloyd and Caroline had dressed and eaten breakfast.

"When do you think you'll catch up with William and Charles?" Caroline asked.

"Probably by late afternoon," Lloyd replied. "I told them that they could expect me about ten miles the other side of Fort Lapwai. They probably made it that far yesterday."

Just then, John Carter and Eliza came in the house from the chicken pen. Each child was cradling a half dozen eggs. Caroline quickly took the eggs from each child and placed them in a bowl. She then sent Eliza to put them away in the root cellar.

John Carter took hold of Lloyd's right hand. "Are you going to fight Indians, Papa?" he asked.

"No, son," Lloyd said. "Papa is going to make some money, so he can take real good care of you, your sister, and mommy."

"Will you be back tomorrow, Papa?"

"No, son." Lloyd glanced at Caroline, then quickly away, when he saw her "see what I mean" look.

Just then Eliza came back from the root cellar. "Papa, would you bring me something pretty back from the wilderness?" she asked.

Lloyd tousled her blond hair. "What would you like Papa to bring, darlin'?" Lloyd asked.

"Anything that's pretty. Mr. Beachy said there are a lot of pretty and beautiful things in the wilderness."

"Well, Mr. Beachy is right about that," Lloyd said. "How about if I bring you a real pretty rock?"

"Okay, Papa, only if it's pretty, though."

Lloyd smiled, then gave both his children a hug and kiss. "Gotta go," he said to Caroline. She followed him out to the front yard, where his saddle horse, Robert E. Lee, was tied. Lloyd had named his horse after the famous Confederate general, the day Fort Sumter had been fired upon.

Lloyd mounted the horse, then bent down and gave Caroline a kiss. She handed him the .44 repeater that Hill had given him. Lloyd checked his watch, it was now 10:00 A.M. The picture of Caroline smiled at him from the inside lid. Lloyd put the watch in his breast pocket. "I'm keeping you next to my heart all the while I'm gone," he said to Caroline. He turned Lee around and rode off. He didn't look back. He didn't want the children to see tears in his eyes.

Caroline went back in the house and dug an old army picture of Lloyd out of a cedar chest. Lloyd was about twenty years old in the photograph. He had been a lieutenant then, serving in the Army during the war with Mexico. She placed the photograph on the lamp stand near her bed. She would never place it back in the cedar chest.

The strangers, Renton and Romain, inquired about passage fare on the *Lewiston* for a trip to Portland. They complained that it was too much. Hill Beachy overheard them cursing and grumbling. He also watched them ferry their horses across the river and ride west toward the coast. *Well, at least that's two toughs who won't be meeting Lloyd on the trail.* He shuddered with a chill on the back of his neck, as he remembered his nightmarish dream.

7

Elk City

Saturday, August 15, 1863

Eastern Theater—Some 450 soldiers drag an 8-inch, 200 pounder Parrott rifle into the battery on Morris Island. It is christened the "Swamp Angel." All day soldiers ferry up the huge quantities of powder and shot required for long-range fire on Charleston. Meanwhile, the Union cannon in an emplacement in the north of the island begin a week-long bombardment of Fort Sumter. By concentrating their fire over such a period, the union artillery officers hope to prevent any Confederate attempt at repairing the fort. Many of Sumter's cannons have already been removed to safer, sand and log batteries ashore, but the garrison returns fire with the remaining armament. Private John Drury, First South Carolina Artillery, replaces the Confederate flag several times until the 80-foot flagstaff is brought down by the bombardment.

In 1861, Lance Monson prospected up the Clearwater River. Coming from the gold fields at Orofino and Pierce, he led over fifty miners up the south fork of the Clearwater. They met several bands of Nez Perce Indians, and, although there was no real trouble, the Indians made it clear that the miners were not welcome. They became even more resentful of the miners, as they started using the Nez Perce Trail as a highway into and across the Bitterroot Mountains and the gold fields of Montana.

By early summer of 1861, however Elk City had become the first mining town of Idaho County. Less than two years later, Lloyd had built his store and purchased a small ranch on the lush meadows surrounding the community.

Lloyd knew he could supply his store in Elk City from Lewiston. He intended to pasture horses, mules, and cattle on his ranch and maybe start a freight business between Elk City and the Clearwater River. There was already talk of bringing a railroad to Lewiston and maybe up the Clearwater. Even if they didn't bring in the railroad, Lloyd figured that riverboats could get up the Clearwater past Lewiston, at least another fifty miles. Either way, he could supply the store in Elk City with his own freight line, besides reaching farther into the wilderness with his pack string. If he was successful in politics, Lloyd believed he could run his business from Lewiston, with the help of Charles Allen and William Phillips. He might even give John Wick twenty-five percent, if the man proved reliable and trustworthy.

Since Monson had arrived with his miners, hundreds more had come and many more were on the way. With the new gold discoveries in Florence and the Boise Basin, the population decreased significantly, but Lloyd was not worried. Miners were a transient bunch and many would return. Even if they didn't, there was still enough activity in Elk City and the eastward wilderness to be called a boom.

Lloyd owned a one-hundred-sixty-acre meadow land ranch at the very east edge of Elk City. Lester Morgan ran it for him. Lester and Lloyd had met in Portland and traveled from there to Lewiston together. Lloyd liked Lester and was saddened when his right leg was permanently injured by a rolling freight wagon, only a week after they arrived in Lewiston. Besides mining, Lester had worked on numerous ranches in Texas and Arizona, so when Lloyd bought the Elk City ranch, Lester was the perfect choice. Even though he couldn't walk or be on his feet for extended hours, he could still ride a horse and he knew the cattle business.

This winter Lloyd would supply nearly fifty percent of the beef the miners would consume. The beef, however, was not in all that great a demand, because many miners preferred elk. Elk meat was just as tasty and much cheaper than Lloyd's and the other ranchers' beef. Lloyd himself actually preferred elk to beef.

It was late afternoon on August 15th, when Lloyd arrived at his Elk City ranch.

"Howdy," Lester said, as Lloyd dismounted near the front of the one-room log cabin.

"Hello, Lester," Lloyd returned. Smiling, he said, "This trip gets longer every time I make it."

Lester nodded in agreement. "Where's your men and mules?" Lester asked.

"Couple miles back," Lloyd replied. "I rode on ahead to see if Maxwell can take fifteen head of mules in his pasture and corrals. I've got about a third of my animals that needs shoeing. Should have had it done before I come in here, but you know how things go."

"Yea, I do," Lester replied. "If Maxwell can do it, I'll help him, but tell you the truth, Lloyd, I ain't seen him around in the last couple of days. I've heard rumors that he was thinking about getting out of the blacksmith business and trying his hand at mining."

"Wouldn't surprise me," Lloyd said as he shook Lester's hand. "Seems like everyone is getting the gold fever."

"Yea, that's true. I would be out there, too, if it wasn't for this bum leg," Lester said.

"How is the leg?" Lloyd asked.

"'Bout the same, still can't bend my knee. Don't suppose

63

I'll ever be able to, hurts like hell when I try. Anyway," Lester said, "here I am chewing the fat, while you're probably starving. Go on in, I've got a stew on the stove. You go ahead and eat while I ride over to Maxwell's. If he can take the mules, then I'll ride back and help Bill and Charles get them in. If not, we'll bring 'em here."

"Thanks," Lloyd said. "I am starved, haven't eaten since this mornin'. Charles and Bill will be hungry. Do you suppose there's enough for them, too?" Lloyd asked.

"More than enough," Lester said, as he swung up on Lloyd's tired Dun. "I'll be back in an hour or less," he said and rode off toward town.

As Lester Morgan rode through town, he saw John Wick standing in the supply store, talking to two rough-looking men. Lester noticed that one of the men wore a pair of .44 Remington army revolvers with crossed gunbelts. The holsters holding both weapons were tied to the thighs of the wearer. Lester looked long and hard at this man. *Strange,* he thought, *I haven't seen anyone wear two guns around their waist since I left Texas, and the only ones that wore them then were usually Rangers or desperadoes. The bad men around these parts usually carry a 12-gauge shotgun loaded with double ought buck shot. I'll stop and talk to John after I check with Maxwell,* he thought. *Maybe I can learn something about this fellow.*

After Lester got permission from Maxwell to bring the mules to the corrals, he returned by the Magruder and Wick Mining Supplies store. He saw that the store was empty and noticed a closed sign in the window. Lester rode on out of town toward where he would find the trail-weary Allen and Phillips.

"What the hell are you coming here for?" Wick barked at the two men. "I told you not to contact me here. It's important we are not seen together."

"How in hell we supposed to get a hold of you then?"

the one wearing the two guns asked.

Wick ignored him. "There's a cabin along the road about one mile south of town. I'll meet you there in twenty minutes," He said.

Just then, Wick saw Lester Morgan ride by. Morgan was looking hard at him, or at least he was looking hard at David Renton and James Romain.

Wick swore. "Don't look around," he ordered the pair. "There's a man out there who knows me and I don't want him to see you. Damn, you guys were supposed to wait until night before you contacted me."

"Thought we'd better do it now," Romain said. "Magruder's in town."

"What! Where?" Wick asked. "Never mind," he continued. "Leave now. I'll meet you at the cabin."

John Wick waited fifteen minutes after the toughs left, then he opened the door to leave. He saw Lester Morgan riding back down the street, so he shut the door and put the "closed" sign up. He hid behind his desk. After Morgan rode by, he slipped out the back door and walked up the street to Maxwell's boarding corrals. He saddled his horse and rode out of town. His thoughts raced, as he suppressed his anger at Renton and Romain.

Why in hell is Magruder here now? In his last letter, he said that he should arrive in Elk City around the twentieth of August. "Well, whatever," he said aloud to himself. "He's here now. I'm just going to have to move this along and that means getting Renton and Romain out of town tonight!"

Romain and Renton were waiting outside on the cabin porch, when he rode up.

"Where's your horses?" Wick asked.

"Out back, in the trees," Romain said. Wick nodded with approval, then dismounted and led his mare into the trees.

"You got any coffee or grub?" Renton asked. "We are

starved, haven't eaten in two days."

"You'll have to wait till it's dark," Wick said. "Come into town then and meet me in the back room of the store. I'll feed you there."

The men shrugged. They were both hungry, but they were also used to hardships, in fact, it was a way of life for them.

"Don't suppose we could get a bath and bed to sleep in, then," Renton said.

"Not a good idea," Wick said. "You can have all the luxury you want after this is over. Until then, you're just gonna have to put up with it."

"That's fine for you to say," Romain said. "You don't have to sleep out on the trail every night, eating hardtack."

"Quit your grumbling, you're going to be well compensated. Now let's quit complaining and get down to business, because I need to get back to the store. I'm sure Magruder is going to be there soon.

"Now, were you able to learn anything about Magruder's plan?"

Romain responded first. "Yea, what you heard several months back is true. When Magruder and his men were in the bath house at Lewiston, we heard them talking. Seems that Magruder is taking a pack train of supplies clear over to the gold camps in Virginia City. On the way back, they're gonna meet some fellows who apparently have a hell of a lot of gold ore. We didn't hear the names of these other men, but Magruder and his outfit are going to meet them on his return trip through Bannack City. Appears they will take on a couple of hired gunmen that these big hot-shot mining people think a lot of. Seems they also trust Magruder and are going to be supporting him for Territorial Delegate one of these days."

"Where is he gonna take the gold ore?" Wick asked.

"Taking it to Elk City. From there, he'll transport it to

Lewiston in wagons, over the new freight road on the Clear-water."

"Did you hear how much ore he expects to be bringing?" Wick asked.

"Quarter million is what we heard," Renton said.

All three looked at each other. This was much more than Wick had believed. He had overheard Magruder talking with the miners in the store last fall and the figure he heard then was one hundred thousand.

"Did anyone see you around Magruder or did Magruder see either of you?" Wick asked.

"No one saw us, 'cept that woman who runs the Luna House," Romain replied. "Maybe her husband saw us from a distance, but there is no reason for him to be suspicious about anything. We didn't go anywhere and didn't see anyone that we know. When we left, we asked about fare on the riverboat to Portland. If anyone was watching, they saw us cross the river on a ferry and ride west toward the coast. We didn't come back and ford the river until way after dark. Even then, we rode around Lewiston. We only saw a half dozen people on the trail coming here, but they aren't going to remember us."

Wick listened to all of this without saying anything, then asked, "You know how I want it done, don't you?" Before Romain could answer, Wick said, "It's got to look like Indians. Use axes or knives and wear these." Opening a closet, Wick withdrew a large leather bag. Inside were four pairs of moccasins and several knives.

"Wear the moccasins and drop at least one of the knives," he said. "After the job is done, use the mules and bring the gold to Granite Springs. Bury the gold there. I can get wagons that far next spring. After you bury the gold, scatter the mules. Take Magruder's horses off the trail at least a mile, then shoot them. I don't want anyone seeing you with them. He's

67

too well known and so will be his horses."

"We heard all this before, John. Don't you think we can follow instructions?" Renton asked.

"If I didn't think you could, I would not be talking to you now," Wick snapped. "I just want to make sure there are no slip-ups. Now, two more things I want to discuss. Listen to me, both of you. Besides the gold ore, Magruder will be carrying over thirty thousand dollars in gold dust and nuggets. I know how much he will be carrying, because I made out the order for supplies that he's taking to Virginia City. He's also told me how much he expects to be bringing, so I expect you to bring that amount here. At that time we will split it three ways. I'll hire you boys as freighters and next spring, the three of us will simply go over and retrieve the gold and take it on to Lewiston, then Portland for delivery under an assumed name. The miners who hired Magruder will think it long gone by that time."

After Wick finished, Romain asked, "What about the two guys over to Bannack City I hired to help us?"

Wick thought for a moment. "When you get to Granite Springs, kill them and bury them with the gold."

8

Jess O'Grady

Tuesday, August 18, 1863
The South—Former U.S. Secretary of War and lately Confederate General John B. Floyd, dies at Arlington, Virginia.

Lloyd Magruder had been in Elk City for three days and had given that many political speeches. He had handed out nearly half of his one thousand brochures that described himself and his views. He had shaken over five hundred hands and answered nearly that many questions.

It seemed that every miner Lloyd met supported him. He was well liked and everyone believed, as his brochure read, "Magruder, The Miner's Choice, The Miner's Voice!" Everywhere Lloyd went, men were clapping him on the back and wanting to buy him drinks.

Everyone, except John Wick and a drunken miner by the name of Jess O'Grady, that is.

Jess O'Grady didn't really have any political views. In fact, Jess O'Grady didn't really have any constructive goals or views on anything. While most miners had filed on two or more claims, O'Grady had filed only one. That claim, he only worked enough to provide himself with liquor and scarlet women. When O'Grady got really drunk, he became belligerent and combative. All of his repressed resentments and anger toward the abusive stepfather of his childhood surfaced. In fact, his resentments would surface and be directed toward anyone who might represent authority over him.

Such was the case August 18th, 1863, the day Lloyd Magruder had his first and only political battle. It was also the day Jess O'Grady stopped being angry.

Lloyd had just stepped down from a platform that the miners had constructed from boards and pickle barrels. As Lloyd began talking with a group of miners, Jess O'Grady stumbled out of "Toby's" saloon, a building constructed from canvas and lodge-pole pine. O'Grady was very drunk, and, although he didn't hear Lloyd speaking, he did hear the miners shouting and applauding Lloyd, as he concluded his speech. This enraged O'Grady. He had gulped down his drink and slammed his glass down on the bar hard enough to break it. O'Grady pushed his way out of the saloon and through a group of miners. Weaving his way through the crowd, O'Grady worked his way to where Lloyd was speaking. When he was within ten feet of Lloyd, O'Grady stopped and bellowed his first criticism.

"You want to build a road, you want to start a freight line, you want to start a railroad, you want to start a steamboat line. Shiiiit—you want a lot, don't you, Mr. Big City Man."

Lloyd and the other men turned and looked at the red-faced O'Grady. For a moment, no one spoke, then O'Grady, realizing that he had become the center of attention of several hundred miners, let loose his second barrage of criticism. "You are a lyin', cheatin', hot-air son of a bitch," he screamed.

"Why don't you shut up, O'Grady?" one of the miners near Lloyd said.

"Why don't you let the coward, big city politician speak for himself?" O'Grady said. With slurred and thick words, he continued. "Why don't we listen to the big city, hot-air coward try to talk his way out of getting his ass whipped in front of a bunch of real men," O'Grady boasted.

Lloyd knew he couldn't reason with this drunk. He had seen other men like this one before. He also knew, as ridiculous as it was, that he couldn't walk away from this man. Not in a frontier gold camp. Not in front of several hundred men, who placed a high value on a man's personal courage and integrity.

Seeing that several miners were now looking at Lloyd and suspecting that his silence was fear, O'Grady pressed on. "I hear tell," he said, "that our Mr. Magruder supports the Confederate cause. I hear tell that Mr. Magruder high-tailed it when the war broke out, 'cause he didn't support the cause to where he would fight for it. No, all Mr. Magruder can do is spout a bunch of hot air and run, just like he's fixin' to do right now. He's gonna talk all of you into gettin' him elected, then he's gonna take your money, then he's gonna run like hell for San Francisco or some such place, and leave you all up here without a freight line, supplies, or anything else he's promised. I've read his little brochures. 'The miner's voice,' it says. Well, he's not my voice and he's not my choice," O'Grady screamed. "He's nothin' but a lyin' coward. I'm surprised he's not wearing a dress." Every miner was now looking at Lloyd.

"Mister, I don't know what your problem is," Lloyd said.

"Oh, now look," O'Grady continued, "he's going to ask me to apologize."

"No," Lloyd said. "Even if you apologized, I would still whip your loud mouth all over this street. Here in a few minutes," Lloyd continued, "everyone here is going to see who really wears a dress. Everyone is going to see who really is a hot-air coward."

"Sam," Lloyd turned and addressed one of the miners. "Would you run up the street to 'Maggie's' and get me one of her prettiest dresses. One that will look real nice on our friend here. Something that will show a little leg."

Sam grinned, and other miners started laughing. The grin on O'Grady's face left. He hadn't expected this. He felt awkward. Now that he had lost the initiative and for the first time, he felt a little fear. The humiliation of being put in a dress in front of several hundred miners was too great a shame to bear. He wouldn't let that happen, but for the first time, he also wished that he had kept his mouth shut. He suddenly wondered *"What the hell"* he was doing out in the street, insulting a man he didn't even know. He really got scared, when a miner behind him said, "Hey, Jess, once you get the dress, you gonna start working at Maggie's?"

Everyone laughed at that and O'Grady's face turned red with anger and embarrassment. He looked rapidly from side to side, as though looking for an ally. "You people wait," he screamed. "You'll see who'll be wearing a dress." His Irish accent, normally undetected, was very pronounced now. "You just wait. I'll be whippin' the lad's ass, you'll see."

O'Grady had turned his back to Lloyd and was screaming at some miners who had just tried to lift his pant legs. Lloyd tapped O'Grady on the shoulder, and, when he turned around, Lloyd hit him in the mouth with a round house right. The blow split O'Grady's lower lip and sent him reeling backwards several steps before he hit the ground flat on his back. It didn't knock him out, but thousands of little lights exploded in O'Grady's head.

O'Grady struggled to his feet and Lloyd hit him with a left hook, then another overhand right. O'Grady fell with a thud and didn't stir. He was unconscious.

Lloyd watched him for several moments, then bent down and pulled off the man's shirt and trousers. O'Grady lay unconscious, spread-eagled in his long johns. When Sam Beck returned, pushing his way through the crowd of miners, he was carrying a bright red dress. The hem line was above the knees and the neck line was very low. Beck presented this dress to Lloyd. Lloyd grinned, as the miners exploded in laughter when he took it and pulled it down over the unconscious man.

Still laughing, several of the miners decided further humiliation was in order for the belligerent, unconscious O'Grady. They packed O'Grady back up the street to Maggie's, where they took him inside. "We are returning your dress," one of the miners said to the smiling Maggie, who stood in the waiting area of the brothel with several of her girls.

"Where can we put this gent, Maggie?" asked another.

"Put him in Rose's room," Maggie said. "He's used to that room, 'cept he's never been in it as a working girl before," Both the miners and girls roared at that one.

"Well, I'm not paying him anything," Rose giggled, and everyone laughed again.

Lloyd had walked over to his store, grinning at the departing figure of Jess O'Grady, clad in a red dress and being carried over the heads of several miners toward Maggie's.

John Wick was standing on the porch when Lloyd got to the store. "Quite a show you put on, Lloyd," Wick said, as Lloyd stood beside him and the two of them watched as the miners disappeared inside the brothel, with O'Grady flopping at full mast.

"Yah, one I wish I could have avoided, though," Lloyd said, soberly.

At that moment, John Wick couldn't have hated Lloyd Magruder any more. He was hoping that O'Grady would have whipped him, humiliated him, even destroyed him. Wick had to struggle in order to obtain and keep an "I'm on your side and friendly" attitude toward Lloyd. His every nerve and muscle fiber wanted to reach out and crush Lloyd's face.

How can the man be so lucky at everything? He thought.
"Did you hear me?" Lloyd asked.

"Huh? What?" Wick said. "I'm sorry, Lloyd. I didn't hear you. I was thinking about the new inventory you brought in."

"That's what I was talking about," Lloyd said. "I'm going to leave a quarter of the supplies here at the store and the rest I'll take on to Virginia City. Are you up to date on the books?" Lloyd asked.

"No, I'm not, Lloyd, but I will be by the time you get back."

"Okay," Lloyd said, "but you will have to have them complete by that time. I'll need that information. I need to plan my next year's budget and inventory, and I won't be back the next time until spring. I may move Caroline up here with me by then," he added.

Wick suppressed an angry objection. Instead, he asked, "When will you get back here from Virginia City, Lloyd?"

"No later than the middle of October," Lloyd said. "I want to be out of these mountains before snow flies."

"Don't blame you there," Wick said. "Yah, no problem. I'll have everything in order by the time you get back."

"Okay. Well, I'm going over to the ranch. I'll have Phillips and Allen bring your inventory over after a while."

"Okay, Lloyd, I'll be here. By the way, business is really good and getting better." A little buttering up never hurt, Wick thought.

"That's great," Lloyd said, as he walked out. Something about Wick didn't set right. Lloyd was starting to wish he had listened to Caroline about Wick. She hadn't liked him from the start. Caroline thought him to be greedy and probably dishonest, and Lloyd was starting to get the same feeling.

He wondered why he hadn't noticed this when he worked for the man in Marysville. *I suppose you see people differently, when they work for you,* he thought to himself.

After Lloyd rode off toward his ranch, Wick slugged the wall and kicked out a side panel in his desk, which he had repaired only three weeks ago, after an earlier fit of anger.

Wick ascended the stairs. He needed to see his anger, needed to mold it and direct it. Wick needed to destroy. Wick slid the wooden box out from under his bed. Unlocking it, he retrieved his journal. He flipped past the pages of his most recent entries, the entries describing his conversations and plans with Renton and Romain.

He turned to the next blank page. Taking a pencil, he began to write. Even though his hand was trembling in anger, his thoughts were precise.

August 18th, 1863—Elk City
Today I thought that smug look on Magruder's face was going to be knocked off. I was really hoping Jess O'Grady would nail his hide to the barn door. NO SUCH LUCK. That damned O'Grady was drunk and Magruder knocked hell out of him. I think the son of a bitch actually got more votes coming his way for knocking O'Grady out. Then humiliating him that way! God, How can that smug son of a bitch get away with that?

He won't, for I've told Renton to cut his damned head off. I truly wish I could be there when Renton and Romain get through with him. I wish I could tell him that I'm the one who killed him. I wish I could tell his wife that I killed him and took all the gold he was saving for her. I wish I could tell her that she could have only 15% of her husband's lousy carcass, because the wolves got the rest and shit him out on some mountain ridge. The BITCH, BITCH, BITCH.

Wick was preparing to start another page in his journal when he heard a BOOM. Sounded like a pistol shot, he thought. He walked to the front door of his store and looked up the street. He saw a crowd of miners gathering at the front of Maggie's. Wick walked up the street and maneuvered his way into the crowd.

At about that time, Maggie came out. Her large bosom, more than half exposed, was heaving with rapid breaths. "It's my fault," she said. "We were just making a joke on O'Grady."

"What's happened, Maggie?" Sam Beck asked.

Rosey Sinclair, standing behind Maggie, spoke first. "O'Grady's done kilt hisself in my room," she said. "After you boys plopped him in bed, I figured us girls would have a little fun, so we stripped him down and turned him on his stomach. Ted Card was still passed out drunk up in Mildred's room, so I had the girls strip him and tote him to my room, where they laid him on top of O'Grady. I guess all the commotion woke O'Grady up. Anyway, when O'Grady saw that he and Ted were naked in the same bed together, he just went kinda crazy.

"Connie had greased up O'Grady's backside and put Ted's hand in the lard bucket. I guess O'Grady saw that and couldn't take things anymore, 'cause he grabbed my Derringer out of the dresser drawer and shot hisself through the head." Rosey told all this without any emotion and continued with the same uninvolved narration. "Ted's still in there, asleep in my bed, and he's got blood all over him. If you boys could tote O'Grady out of here, us girls will clean things up and get Ted awake and dressed."

"Yea," Maggie spoke up. "I don't want another one killing hisself in here, bad for business, you know."

Several of the miners went inside and got O'Grady's body. Wick noticed that other than the red dress, which was pulled up and covering only his neck, he had nothing else on. Wick walked away in disgust, as the miners carried O'Grady's body toward Maxwell's barn, which doubled as a community funeral parlor, due to the many tack rooms inside.

Wick turned from the scene in disgust, wondering if the miner's court would even sit in council on O'Grady's cowardly death. *Probably not,* he thought, *the damn miners helped kill O'Grady. DAMN.* He hated this godforsaken wilderness and all the people in it.

Wick ascended the steps back to the store and went back to his journal. He wrote:

August 18th—Continued
   As I was writing in this journal, the fool O'Grady killed himself in the whore house, all because of a joke the whores pulled on him. The whores, the miners and Magruder, they are all in the same class. They all need to be destroyed.

As John Wick was writing in his journal, Sam Beck and several other miners were holding funeral services for O'Grady at Maxwell's barn. That is, they were dividing up O'Grady's property among themselves, as they were in agreement, no relatives of O'Grady's were known. They also agreed that different miners, on different days, would work O'Grady's mine. They decided to bury O'Grady on his mine, which was located about one mile south of Elk City, near the Nez Perce Trail. Beck asked a young miner, by the name of Francis Goodwin, to write something on a head board, "so that all of us can remember the poor unfortunate O'Grady."

Goodwin, a young man of twenty-one, who decided to pursue wealth instead of education, and had dropped his schooling at Harvard a year before, agreed to so honor the poor man. Several months before, O'Grady had hit Goodwin over the head with a very hard bottle from Toby's Saloon. In light of that, Goodwin wrote the following eulogy for his now departed acquaintance:

Here lies Jess O'Grady,
Tough and Rough as any old lady.
He died in bed with Ted,
By his own hand, shot through the head.

Although he wasn't courageous,
He died outrageous.
A dress of red over his head,
a bucket of lard,
stuck in his back yard.

9

Lester Morgan

Saturday, August 22, 1863

The South—President Davis offers an amnesty to Confederate soldiers absent without leave. The chronic desertion rate in the Southern armies has to be arrested soon or the already large Union forces will be unbeatable. In fact, Union armies have similar problems.

John Wick was particularly interested in the number of mules Lloyd and his men were leaving Elk City with. If his count had been correct, there were one hundred twenty-three mules. A hell of a lot of animals, even for experienced packers like Magruder and Company. Wick was even more interested, then delighted, when he saw Lester Morgan riding with the pack string.

"Outstanding," Wick said aloud. "Magruder needs Morgan to help with that many mules. He's taking Morgan to Virginia City."

Wick smiled at this unexpected opportunity. With Morgan gone, he could go over to the ranch and look through Magruder's desk. Maybe he could learn more about the business. Maybe he could even find some cash for operating expenses. Wick smiled. "They sure won't need it on their return trip." He pulled the shades on the store front windows, then hung out the "Closed" sign.

Three miles out of town, Magruder and Morgan halted and dismounted. "Appreciate your help with the ranch and all, Lester," Lloyd said. "You're doing a hell of a job. On my way back, we'll talk partnership."

"I'm interested, Lloyd," Lester replied. The men shook hands and Lloyd remounted after tightening his saddle hitch.

"Remember what I said, Les, if you will. Keep an eye on Wick for me. I think he may be up to something and I'm getting so I don't trust him. I don't know what it is, but he sure seems reluctant to produce the business books. I've told him that I expect them to be completed when I get back."

"Know what you mean, Lloyd," Lester said. "I haven't trusted the man every since I met him. He's unsociable as hell, won't even speak to me unless he needs something. Acts like I'm trespassing anytime I go into the store. I would have told him where to go if it wasn't necessary to work with him. I'm really wondering about him, Lloyd, he's up to something. Those two toughs talking to him in the store the other day weren't miners, Lloyd. They were gunmen. I've seen that kind before in Texas, during the range wars."

"When I get back," Lloyd said, "I'll have a real close look at Mr. Wick, and what he's up to. Would have done it this time, if I hadn't been so busy getting these damn mules shod. Then of course that thing with O'Grady."

"That wasn't your fault, Lloyd," Lester responded. "That was O'Grady's all the way."

"Yah, well, maybe you could ask Sam Beck to take O'Grady's head board down. That's something that's just gonna keep this thing alive and I don't really want to be remembered as part of O'Grady's flamboyant demise."

Lester grinned. "I'll do it, Lloyd, and in the meantime, be careful. Some of the trail through the Bitterroots is almighty hell, especially with a hundred twenty-three mules."

Lloyd nodded. "I've got the two best packers in the world. If they can't get the mules through, it can't be done. Anyway, thanks again, Lester, and thanks for riding a ways with me, enjoyed your company."

"Likewise, Lloyd," Lester said, as he remounted and turned his bay back toward Elk City.

Lloyd pulled his pocket watch out. The picture of Caroline smiled up at him. He felt a twinge of loneliness as he studied her picture. "I love you," he whispered, then spurred his horse ahead to catch up with the pack string.

Lester Morgan road back through Elk City at eleven o'clock that morning. The first thing that he paid attention to was the "closed" sign hanging on the door of Magruder and Wick mining Supplies. The next thing was the shades that were pulled down.

Lester looked at his watch. *11:00 A.M. What day is this?* He thought. *Saturday! What the hell is Wick closed for now? He's only supposed to be closed on Sundays. I'm sure this is August 22nd, Saturday.*

Lester dismounted and tied his horse at the rail in front of the store. The front door was locked, but he used the key Lloyd had given him and went in. The interior was dimly lighted, so Lester raised the shades. "John," he called, "you here?" He called twice more, but got no answer. Lester decided to look upstairs in Wick's living quarters, on the off chance he was asleep or maybe even sick. *First,* he thought, *I wonder if Wick has a calendar around someplace. Maybe this is Sunday.* He went to Wick's desk. No calendar, but there was a journal or a diary. Lester started to turn away, then something on the journal page caught his eye. He picked up the journal and started to read.

August 22, 1863—Saturday
Lloyd Magruder just left town. Good Riddance! I'll never

see him again. He took Lester Morgan with him, too. At last, things are going my way. Now, I'll just ride over to the ranch and look through Magruder's desk. Maybe I can get some clue as to when and where he is going to return from the gold camps with his treasure. Maybe even get some operating money if Morgan still puts his wages in the coffee can under the floor.

God! Morgan thought. *That bastard has spied on me!*

The entry ended with, "These simple bastards are so predictable."

Morgan could hardly believe what he was reading. Quickly, he turned the pages to read more. The next entry was August 18th. This was the entry in which Wick had described Magruder's fight with O'Grady and O'Grady's later suicide.

Lester turned back more pages, almost frantically. He could hardly comprehend the hate and viciousness he was reading. The next entry read:

Saturday—June 13th, 1863
    Met an old acquaintance and one of his friends today. James Romain and his friend, David Renton. I like Romain's style. He's good with a gun and not afraid to use it. I know for a fact he's killed two men. He would probably kill more, if I had the money.
    He tells me that he and his friend quit the army. They had to leave because the Union Army hangs deserters.
    We had a few drinks at Toby's, told him I wanted to offer him a proposition and to see me at the store tomorrow. Said he would, but who knows about that type. Especially his friend, David Renton, that one gives me the creeps.

Sunday—June 14th, 1863
    Met with Renton and Romain today—told them of my plan—told them if they could take it from Magruder, I could get it out of the country. Didn't tell them I would use Magruder's own freight line and money to do it. Told them to use

axes on Magruder and company. I want it to look like Indians, as this is an excellent time to blame it on them. Everyone knows they are angry about the miners using their trail across the Bitterroots. Right where Mr. Magruder is heading. Yes, Sir, right into an Indian ambush. Ha Ha, an ambush anyway. With Magruder out of the way, I'll take over his business. Tell his wife or anyone who asks that I had to sell the business in order to pay off all the other bills. After all, who does the books around here? Ha Ha.

Even with a three-way split, I'll still be rich. Have to watch out for Magruder's ranch partner, though. He seems a little nosy. If he gets too nosy, guess he can be dealt with.

Romain tells me that he needs two other men to help him with the job. Says he already has two that he can trust. I told him I don't care what he wants to do, I just don't want to meet them and I don't want him to even mention my name. Told him that if he does, the deal is off. He didn't like it when I told him that he had to pay them out of his share of the gold.

Lester stood there for a long time, or at least what seemed like a long time. Finally, he realized John Wick was planning murder and robbery, had in fact, set in motion the plan for doing that. Those two men he had seen in the store with Wick, must have been Romain and Renton.

God! Lester said to himself, *Wick is probably at the ranch this very moment. I better get out there and bring Mr. Wick back to town. I'll turn him and his little journal here over to the miner's court. Soon as I can get someone to hold this bird for me, I'll ride hell fire and tell Lloyd about this. God, hope I'm not too late.*

Lester turned around, snapping the journal shut. He stared into a cocked Colt .45 revolver, held by John Wick.

"Thought you were riding with Magruder," Wick said. "It's too bad you didn't stay with him, now I've got a problem. What do I do with you. Mr. Morgan?"

Lester casually dropped the journal down and held it behind his right thigh, but Wick caught the movement. "Give me that damned book," he snapped.

Lester handed it to him, realizing that this was no time to provoke a very sick and dangerous man. He would bide his time and make his move as soon as Wick pointed the big revolver in another direction.

"Look, John," Lester said, "there's no need for this thing to go any further, so far, no one has been hurt and it can be stopped right now. Just get on your horse and go. I won't try and stop you, but I will ride to warn Lloyd."

"You won't ride and warn anybody," Wick replied. "In fact, if you don't do as I tell you right now, I'm gonna blow a hole through your chest. Now, shut up and sit in that chair."

Lester did as he was told. The big .44 Colt hadn't wavered an inch. Keeping the gun trained on Lester, Wick cut several six-foot lengths of rope from one of the rope rolls in the store. He bound Lester's hands, feet, and chest to the chair. The coils around Lester's hands were so tight that the blood flow to his hands was immediately cut off. His fingers turned blue and started to swell.

"Good God, man! Can't you loosen these ropes just a little?" Lester asked. "I'm not getting any circulation."

"Nor will you," Wick replied. He then grabbed a pick, and with all his might he swung and buried one side to the hilt through the top of Lester's skull. Lester's body jerked and twitched for several moments, as a geyser of blood spewed out the wound and down over his face.

Wick jerked to remove the pick from Lester's skull but found it was stuck. He jerked violently to free the pick and, only after the end punched a hole through the skin in the back of his neck, did it come free. He quickly wrapped then tied gunny sacks around Lester's head to stem the flow of blood. "That much blood on the floor is hard to explain," he said to himself.

Wick calmly walked back to the front of the store and drew the shades back down. He then set about the task of wrapping Lester's body in several pieces of canvas. His thoughts raced, but, to any onlooker, John Wick would have appeared no more excited than a man eating his dinner.

I need to get this body out of here, but where? He thought. *Can't move it until tonight, after dark.*

That's okay. I need time to clean up this mess, get rid of Morgan's horse, what else? Bury him, but where? Then Wick's eye lit up. "Yah," he said aloud, "I'll bury him with O'Grady. No one will notice and besides, O'Grady likes company." He laughed then, a sick demented kind of a cackle laugh, as he dragged Lester Morgan's body inside a storage closet.

10

The Counselor

"Well, what's the date today?" Jim Hays asked.

"It's January 3rd, 1981. Why?"

"Well, why don't you just start with today's date, or if you feel like it, go back a year, even ten years. Just talk to me about whatever you want, whatever you feel. We can get into specifics any time. In fact, why don't we go back a year ago. Didn't you tell me last week, that your grandfather died just a year ago."

"Yes, that's correct, and I guess to date that's the biggest loss I have had in my life."

"Excuse me just a minute, Mr. Kincade," Jim Hays said. "I need to get your file." He walked across the room and opened the door separating his office from that of his secretary's. "Janice, would you get me the Marty Kincade file?" he asked.

Janice, smiling, handed him the file. "As always, Dr. Hays, I'm ready." Jim Hays blushed a little, thanking her, as he closed the door and tried to conceal a smile.

He studied the file, as he walked back to his desk and sat down. "I have notes on several topics or should I say important areas, if you will, grief areas. Do you mind if I summarize them?"

"No, not at all, Doctor," Marty Kincade said. "Go ahead.

Maybe that way I can figure out what I want to talk about first."

Hays studied his notes a little longer. "I'm going to read the list. You stop me or comment whenever you want."

"First of all. I've listed Sandra. That your wife?"

"Yes, it is."

"Then I've got job, promotion, loss. You've just recently got out of police work. I'm wondering if that may be part of what's bothering you?" Hays asked.

"No, yah, I guess maybe a little."

"I'll go on," Hays said, looking back down at his notes. "Alcohol! Wanna try that one?"

"After a while. Okay, Doc?" Marty asked.

"No problem. Shall we go back to your grandfather?"

"Yah, I like that. I need to talk about him."

"Okay," Hays said. "Shoot."

"Well, he—he was my very best fried," Marty said. "From the time I was old enough to remember things, he was there. He taught me how to hunt, fish, and trap. He taught me about right and wrong and always told me, that to get things done, one sometimes has to improvise or go a different route in order to accomplish a goal. He told me about sex and women, and he told me a lot about life in general.

"My family has a cabin in the mountains. That's where my great-grandfather first homesteaded and the place has been in the family now for about ninety years. Grandpa took me to every ridge and draw within fifteen miles of our cabin. He called it 'Learnin' the Country Boy.' He called me and all of my friends Boy, no matter how old we were."

"How old was he when he died?" Hays asked.

"He was eighty-seven and he was active right up until three months before he died," Marty said. "He loved the mountains and wildlife, and people amused him to no end. After I got older, Grandpa would sometimes embarrass me with some of his actions, but I sure did love that old man. If he saw someone who looked or acted a little different, he would stare at them until they got out of sight. Then he would always say, "Well, myyy God, would you look at that." Sometimes he made people mad with his staring, but he never did it to agitate them, he was just not really aware how he affected people. Grandpa was definitely a hayseed, but he was a very good man."

"You mentioned hunting and fishing with him. Is that what you miss a lot?" Hays asked.

Marty thought for a moment. "Yah, I miss the hunts a lot, especially when I come across an area where we had a successful hunt together. Last fall I shot a bull elk, and while I was dressing it out, I realized that it was the same place that Grandpa had killed a big bull moose back in 1957. In fact, it was the state record at that time. When I realized where I was at, I just sat on the elk and became lost in thought for probably twenty minutes. That area sure brought back a lot of memories. You know, that old man used to break pine needles and rub them all over his body to conceal his scent when he was hunting. I do that to this day, and it works. If I remember right, I was rubbing pine needles into my skin the day Grandpa shot the moose."

"Let me ask you this," Hays said. "You were in the Vietnam War, is that correct?"

"Yes. That's right," Marty replied.

"While you were away, do you remember if you missed your wife and parents as much as you missed your grandfather?"

Marty thought. "I missed them all, it was just a different kind of missing for each of them. I wrote to my wife and parents more than I did to Grandpa, but I remember thinking of him a lot, especially in hunting season.

"Of course, at that time in my life, things were really

changing for me. I was gaining an independence from my parents, trying to find the responsibility of being a husband and father and at the same time, finding out how to live and survive in the big world. It was quite a culture shock, coming from small town U.S.A. to San Diego, California, then on to the Nam.

"Also, I started drinking a lot. I think maybe that's when I started having a problem with the booze. After I got out of the service, I went into police work and my drinking continued. Especially, when I started working narcotics with a D.E.A. task force."

"Marty, do you think you are an alcoholic?"

There it is, Marty thought, *the question I've been avoiding. The question I never wanted to hear. The question no one has asked, but everyone has hinted at for years.*

"No, of course not, Doc. Why do you ask that?" A defensive tone was rising in Marty's voice.

"Well, in every meeting we've had, you've mentioned alcohol. You just recently lost your job. I believe last week you referred to it as losing your career. If I'm not mistaken, alcohol was involved in the incident that led up to your resignation from the police force. You are separated from your wife, and in your own words, you said that she thinks you drink too much and are seeing other women. All of that is characteristic of alcohol dysfunction."

Marty was silent for several moments, but finally said, "I, I may drink a little too much sometimes, but I'm not an alcoholic, Doc."

"Okay," Hays said. "I just wanted to find out what you feel your status is. You're the only one who can say if you are or not." Marty didn't respond to that, so Hays said, "Let's throw grief into this equation."

Marty looked at him. "What do you mean, Doc?"

"Well," Hays said, "you've come here because you're

upset about leaving police work. You can't sleep and you think maybe I can help with that, right?"

"Well, yah, I guess so," Marty replied, "but what does grief have to do with anything?"

"You have a lot of losses in your life right now, Mr. Kincade. When we have losses, we have grief and when we have grief, we have additional problems, including drinking of alcohol. Unfortunately, too many Americans handle their grief and other problems with alcohol and/or drugs. In dealing with any problem, you first have to identify that problem. Are you with me on that?" Hays asked.

"Absolutely," Marty responded.

"Then," Hays continued, "you have to be honest about that problem and last, but not least, you have to take action with the problem. Now, Mr. Kincade, I'm going to be honest with you. You have to do what I've just described or both of us are just wasting our time. You're paying me twenty-five dollars an hour, so let me help you get your money's worth. Let's deal honestly with each other, Okay?"

Marty stared at Hays for several seconds before he spoke. "I'm in love or at least I was in love with another woman. She was murdered two weeks before I resigned from the force. A week before that, I was, as you probably know from reading the newspapers, involved in a fistfight with a biker."

"Had you been drinking just prior to the fight?" Hays asked.

Marty dropped his head. "Yah, I had been."

Hays looked at Marty for over a minute, without either of them speaking. "Another loss," he finally said. "Let's list your losses for the last year."

"First, your grandfather, your teacher, and best friend. Next, your wife, then your job. The last thing is your girlfriend, except this loss is, in some ways, the worst one of all. You can't talk to anyone about it. How am I doing?" Hays asked.

"Right on target," Marty said remorsefully.

"Mr. Kincade, we need to deal with each of these losses. We also need to deal with yet another loss."

"What's that?" Marty asked.

"The loss of your self-esteem."

Marty looked down again. He didn't really want to deal with all of these feelings. It would be much better to let a little CC and 7 plug the holes.

"I think we need to approach these losses one at a time, just like we did Vietnam two weeks ago. Shall we go back to your grandfather?" Hays asked.

"Yah, guess so," Marty said quietly.

"Good," Hays said. "Then let me ask you this, after your grandfather died, did you ever wish that things could have been better, more or different, in your relationship with him?"

Marty leaned forward in his chair. He placed his elbows on his knees, while he lowered his face into his open palms. Marty spoke slowly, as his thoughts probed memories.

"My relationship with Grandpa was very complete in almost all ways. I don't wish that it was different, and it couldn't have been any better. The more part, . . . well, more time together would have been great. I do wish we would have had more time to find the gold."

"What gold is that, Mr. Kincade?" Hays asked.

"The Bitterroot Gold, Doc. The gold buried somewhere in the Bitterroot Mountains by the outlaw killers of Lloyd Magruder."

"I know about the Bitterroot Mountains, of course, but I'm afraid I'm not well versed in local history," Hays said.

"Grandpa hunted for the gold a good part of his life and starting about age fourteen, I helped him look for it. We took over twenty trips into the wilderness and walked every inch of the Nez Perce Indian Trail from Elk City to the Selway River."

"Wait, wait," Hays said. "Back up and tell me about this

from the beginning. Like I said, I'm not well versed in local history."

"Okay, I'm sorry," Marty said. "I get a little excited when I start thinking about the Lloyd Magruder case. I have an interest in it from two angles."

"And they are?" Hays asked.

"Well," Marty said, "from the treasure hunter's point of view, it would be nice to find all of that gold and live wealthy for the rest of one's life. Secondly, and just as important for me, from an investigator's point of view, I would like to find out how truthful and accurate the testimony of the only eyewitness to this murder was. There was a lot of speculation that the witness, whose name was William Page, did not tell all of the truth or maybe even lied to save his own skin."

"Well, how did this murder and robbery happen?" Hays asked.

"Lloyd Magruder and four of his men were murdered, hacked to death with axes, while they slept at a night camp," Marty explained. "Magruder was a merchant and politician here in Idaho. He was well liked and on his way to becoming quite successful. He was en route from the Montana gold fields with several thousand dollars in gold, traveling back to his store and ranch in Elk City. Some of the men he hired to help him with the pack string turned out to be bandits. Anyway, the bad guys killed all the good guys and took all of their gold.

"There are rumors and Grandpa claimed that he had once read a letter, describing how Magruder may have been packing other miners' gold besides his own. As rumor has it, the outlaws, after killing Magruder and his men, buried the biggest share of the gold back in the Bitterroot Mountains, somewhere along the Nez Perce Indian Trail. Many people have looked for it over the years, but no one has ever found anything."

"Do you think there really is buried gold in those mountains?" Jim Hays asked.

"Yes, I do, Doc. Grandpa believed it and I just wish he was here to help continue looking for it. I guess in this way, our relationship wasn't totally complete."

"Interesting story, Mr. Kincade. I hope it has an ending."

"I believe it does, Doctor Hays," Marty replied. "It just hasn't been told yet."

"There's another story that needs to be told, Mr. Kincade. It's about you, but you're the only one who can tell it. Get through your denial and the story will come smoothly."

Marty Kincade looked at his psychiatrist, who was looking at his watch. Just then Janice knocked, then opened the doctor's door. "Mr. Cole is here, Doctor," she said. Marty rose to leave and caught her wink at the doctor. Marty looked back and noticed that Jim Hays was blushing.

As Marty was leaving, Jim Hays said after him, "Sounds like you had quite a grandfather, Marty."

Grandfather

At this meadow on the mountain,
I know that you are still here.
Your once told wisdom, Grandfather,
is now so clear.

From a boy that I was,
To the man that I am now,
my life so inspired,
memories so much desired.

From the mountains we climbed
and streams we followed,
our acquaintance so complete,
we never had to compete.

93

With the bugle of the bull
in early fall,
we were always there
for our call.

For any whitetail
on the run,
there was always the sound
of our gun.

Though all of the memories
are now in the past,
in my mind
they will never be last.

For now, Grandfather,
you have answered your last call,
But you'll always be with me
in the fall.

11

The Bees, the Trees, and a Cliff

Thursday, September 3, 1863

Western Theater—General Bragg recognizes he is being outmaneuvered again. He remarks to Major Daniel H. Hills, "It is said to be easy to defend a mountainous country, but mountains hide your foe from you, while they are full of gaps through which he can pounce upon you at any time. A mountain is like a wall of a house full of rat holes. The rat lies hidden at his hole to pop out when no one is watching."

The first twenty miles was a pleasant and relaxing ride, even with a hundred twenty-three mules. The going had been easy, as the forest covered relative flat and scattered mountain meadows. The many ridges and draws had been low and shallow. *Much like waves in the ocean,* Lloyd thought. For the most part, the forest in this area looked like a giant well-manicured city park. Lloyd almost expected to suddenly find homes nestled around some of the more beautiful meadows.

What really set the area off from more civilized areas was the abundance of wildlife. Every few hundred yards, they would see herds of elk. Often, whitetail deer would jump from cover and disappear within seconds into the forest.

This morning Lloyd and the others were treated to an unexpected and entertaining sight. The previous evening the men, using picket lines, had pastured the mules and horses in a meadow. They had made camp in an adjacent meadow about seventy-five yards away. As dawn was breaking, Lloyd heard a high-pitched squeal, followed by several guttural grunts. The squeal was immediately answered by another, deeper squeal and grunts, probably one hundred yards from where the first challenge had come.

"Sounds like there's a-goin' to be some fightin' goin' on," Charles Allen said.

Lloyd looked at him, then back toward where the bull elk were preparing for battle. "It sure does," Lloyd said. "I wish we had a camera box. This could really be something."

Bill Phillips, who had just shaved in a small stream, came up to them then. "Sounds like a couple of big fellers, eh, Lloyd?" he said.

"Sure does," Lloyd replied. "Look. There's one now," Lloyd said, pointing. The men saw a large bull with high and long antlers emerge from the timber into the meadow.

Phillips counted seven even tines on each antler. "Boy, he is big," Allen said. Moments later the other bull emerged from the timber onto the other side of the meadow. This bull was equally big, with seven tines on one antler and six on the other.

The coats of both bulls were matted with mud and urine and both animals' antlers sprouted impaled chunks of meadow sod. The bulls stood facing each other, now challenging with sharp barks, instead of bugling.

After several minutes, both bulls lowered their heads. They began circling each other.

Suddenly and violently they clashed together. Both sets of massive antlers locked in combat. The struggle that had begun with time, continued.

The bulls pushed, shoved, and twisted as each tried for advantage over the other. The struggle continued for about

96

twenty minutes. Both bulls were bleeding from shoulder wounds and a white froth covered both of their noses. The animals worked their way across the meadow, twisting, lunging, and parrying. Finally, they approached within fifteen yards of the men's camp. The bulls, enraged with anger and intent with their battle, did not see the men. The men, transfixed with the awesome display of power and the twisting, turning, grunting animals, did not realize, until too late, that they were in the middle of a bull elk battle.

One moment, the bulls had been in the meadow. The next, they were trampling the tent, then the campfire and cooking pot. One bull nearly stepped on the new rifle of Lloyd's, given to him by his friend Hill Beachy. Lloyd grabbed the rifle from where it was leaning on a stump. He levered a round into the chamber and fired into the air. The bulls continued to fight, so he levered another and fired again. The bulls continued, so he chambered and fired two more.

The bulls, finally realizing where they were, ran off in different directions and disappeared in the forest.

Lloyd surveyed his camp. The tent was knocked down, the food boxes tipped over, and the campfire had been stamped out.

"Well, guess those fellers wanted us to break camp," Allen commented.

Lloyd and Bill Phillips smiled at each other. "Damn good entertainment," Lloyd said. "Guess it was worth the price for that kind of a show, nothing really damaged anyway." Within an hour, the men had the mules loaded, lined out, and started down the trail.

"Will we make the Bitterroot River by nightfall?" Lloyd asked Allen, who was in the lead of the first seventy mules.

"Probably," he replied, "unless we have trouble with any of the mules while crossing some of the shale rock that we have to cross."

By noon, the pack train started a decent from what appeared to be the edge of the world. Lloyd thought the view was breathtaking. For nearly a hundred miles, a vast ocean of mountains, trees, and granite rock could be seen. Directly below and to the north of the trail, Lloyd could see two small alpine lakes, perhaps two thousand feet down. The lakes, each an acre or more in size, appeared to be no larger than a small blue puddle of water. Lloyd estimated that they were eight thousand feet above sea level.

The rest of the afternoon was spent climbing and descending smaller ridges and mountain sides in the mammoth Bitterroot Valley. About an hour before dark, Charles Allen came riding back down the line and spoke to Lloyd. "I'm letting the old white mule lead the way down to the river. The others will follow her and she'll stop at the river where we always camp."

"Fine with me," Lloyd said. "I'm starting to get hungry." Looking around, he said, "Guess we could camp right here on this ridge, it's flat and large enough to graze all the stock."

"Be better along the river," Allen said. "We're only about a mile above it and that way we can water the stock and not have to climb back up here for the night."

"Good thought," Lloyd said. "It does appear that a lot of folks do climb back up here, though," Lloyd said, as he pointed to several different circles of rock used for camp fires, and lean-to frames.

"That is where people camp who are traveling toward Elk City from the gold fields. They camp here after watering their stock in the Bitterroot. This is the only ridge for several miles that has a wide enough top to allow for a camp and stock to graze."

Following the seventy mules that Charles had been leading, the men made their descent down the ridge. As they got closer to the river, Lloyd caught glimpses of it through the trees. *A beautiful river,* he thought, *what a paradise this country is. I can understand why the Indian gets upset when we trespass. They say all we do is take and take. They don't understand why we don't live with the earth as they do. If they would try to understand that God put man on earth to use it, maybe we would all get along better. Guess it doesn't really matter, the Indian and White man aren't going to agree on this land for many years, if ever.*

Lloyd was still in deep thought, when Bill Phillips cried out. Lloyd looked over his shoulder and saw Phillips swatting wildly with his hat. His horse was crow-hopping below the trail and going around the side of the mountain.

"Bees," Phillips screamed, as his horse disappeared behind several large boulders.

Lloyd turned his horse and spurred after the runaway mare. Several mules, near Phillips's original position on the trail, started running, bucking, and kicking, following Phillips's horse around the mountain.

Lloyd turned around the boulder where Phillips had gone, but reined in immediately. He looked straight down. Nearly a thousand feet below, he could see the Little Clearwater River, just above where it merged with the Bitterroot.

At the same time, his vision took in several startling events. The first was a drastic and immediate change in the geographical view. Lloyd was looking at a giant cliff and higher mountains of granite. No trees, just granite rock. It appeared that the peaceful alpine forest had suddenly changed into a vast, empty rock basin.

The next thing Lloyd noticed was that the three mules and Phillips's horse were falling through the air, rapidly, toward the Little Clearwater below. He watched in terror as one of the pack mules struck the side of the canyon wall. He couldn't hear a sound, but he saw shovels, picks, other tools, and a large wooden box separate from the mule's body. Lloyd noticed that the tools seemed to float in slow motion, as they descended, following the no-longer-burdened animal.

At the same time, Lloyd looked into a face filled with horrified fear. Hanging out over the edge of the cliff, was William Phillips. He was clinging to the top half of a five-inch fir tree, which was slowly being pulled from the ground by his weight. Lloyd jerked his horse away from the cliff edge.

"I'm coming, Bill!" Lloyd yelled. Dismounting, he grabbed a fifteen-foot length of rope from his saddle bag. Lloyd tied one end of the rope to the base of the fir tree, which was now dangerously close to breaking free of the soil and rock holding it. The other end Lloyd tied around his saddle horn. As Lloyd made the last half hitch around the horn, the rope went taut. Lloyd looked. The tree had broken free. All but the base was hanging over the side of the cliff.

Lloyd yelled, "Bill, are you okay?" No sound, no reply. Lloyd was starting to panic. He couldn't see Phillips, but realized he must still be clinging to the tree as the rope was taut. Lloyd grabbed the reins and led his horse slowly away from the cliff. In a moment, the tree, then Phillips was dragged back to the top of the cliff. In another moment Phillips was scrambling toward Lloyd as fast as he could on hands and knees.

Phillips stood, trembling, his face white, with no expression, except his eyes, which were wide open and dilated. Phillips didn't say anything. He just stared at Lloyd. Several times his mouth opened and his lower lip trembled, but no sound came out. Lloyd noticed a large and growing wet spot at the crotch of Phillips's pants. Lloyd wanted to laugh, but he wasn't so sure he didn't have a wet spot of his own.

Charles Allen rode to them and dismounted. He could tell something was wrong. Both Lloyd and Bill were still staring at each other, as Charles, noticing one end of the rope tied to Lloyd's saddle and the other to the tree, looked over the edge of the cliff. He looked for a long time, then turned to Lloyd, who was remounting. "Bill's horse, huh?" he said.

Lloyd shook his head, still too shaken to explain much. Lloyd kicked his foot free of the stirrup and offered a hand to Phillips. "Come on, Bill, get up behind me. I'll take you to the river."

The three men rode in silence. When they reached the river, they found the entire string of mules scattered up and down the stream, drinking their fill. Lloyd noticed that several lead ropes were either missing or broken, but all of the packs were intact.

The next hour was spent reorganizing and unloading for the night camp. As he was unsaddling his horse, Charles asked Phillips how he was doing. "Stomach settled down any?"

"Yah, some," he replied. "Never wanta go through something like that again, though."

"What exactly happened, Bill?" Charles asked.

Phillips paused, as Lloyd approached with an arm load of wood. "Well," he began, "I left the trail, for I was going out in the brush for a nature call. Hadn't gone fifteen feet, when my horse stirred up a wasp nest. Anyway, next thing I know, there's bees all over and my mare is going crazy. She takes off a-runnin' and I see she is going over the cliff. I don't even remember grabbin' hold of the tree, but I sure as hell remember holdin' onto it, 'cause them damn mules ran right over the tree and me before they went over the cliff. I thought I was a goner for sure, so I just closed my eyes and crapped my pants. Didn't figger it was gonna matter much anyway, for I knew I was a dyin'. That little tree held though, least ways it held long enough for Lloyd to come along and get a rope on it. Can't say as I've ever been happier to see anyone in my life," Phillips said.

"In the morning we'll ride up river and salvage your saddle and whatever supplies that are intact. It shouldn't be more than a quarter of a mile from here," Lloyd said. The men nodded, as Lloyd knelt to start the evening campfire.

It was a long time before Bill Phillips went to sleep that night. When he could drift away, he was awakened several times. Each time he woke up, it was right before he hit the rocks beside the mules and his horse.

12

The Lone Star

Saturday, September 19, 1863

Western Theater—Under cover of darkness the Confederate forces infiltrate into Rosecrans's Federals.

The attack comes from within, then head on. The battlefield is a vast natural amphitheater bounded by Missionary Ridge and Pigeon Mountain.

The area is densely forested, making command and control a nightmare.

Thomas's Corps bears the brunt of the Confederate attack, but he fights a brilliant defensive action and is still in good order when the fighting dies down.

His gaunt frame is clothed with a faded and worn flannel shirt. His trousers are patched with canvas on the knees and seat. A well-used, sweat-stained slouch hat protects him from the sun. His arms are covered with mosquito bites. His hands are wrinkled and scraped from submersion in cold mountain streams, while working his gold pan.

Tired at dark, he has a supper of salt pork and beans. Occasionally he varies his meals with dried apples and elk meat.

Sleeping on the cold damp ground, working with sore and aching muscles, and fighting loneliness and homesickness, the miners struggle on. Day after day, week after week, the same hard backbreaking work. Some leave, some die, some simply move to other gold fields.

A few, a very few, strike it rich. Such was the case with Don Seibel, John Hansen, and Gary Trent. The three men were partners, had been for a long time. Their days as Indian fighters and Texas Rangers had bonded the men into an unbreakable friendship. They had saved each other's life, drunk the same whiskey, loved the same women, and now they shared the same fortune. It had happened the previous summer in July. Trent and Hansen were working the sluice, while Seibel removed the dirt and gravel from the mine tunnel. For months they had taken an ounce of gold a day.

On July 18th of 1862, that changed. Seibel had taken up his pick and like hundreds of times before, sunk one side to the hilt in the wall of the tunnel. This time though, the feel was different. The rock was hard, yet yielding. A close inspection of th rock revealed that Seibel had found a six foot by twenty foot vein of nearly pure gold. Since then, they had found eight more such veins. Some had been four or five inches thick, but three of the veins had been over five feet through.

The men had put their gold into dynamite boxes. They stored the boxes in a hole, dug under their cabin. Subsequently, they had constructed a rough-hewn log floor, which other miners thought was foolish, since it was a home only to be used seven months out of the year. Nevertheless, several other miners also constructed wood floors in their cabins.

The men had told no one of their find. No one, that is, except Lloyd Magruder and Lester Morgan. They had known Morgan in Texas. They liked and trusted Morgan. During one of their Indian campaigns, Morgan had supplied their company with horses in searching for the ever-elusive Apache. Morgan had earned their real respect when he turned over three thousand dollars in cash to them. He had found the money in a metal box, removing it from a burned-out wagon left behind by an Apache war party. The settlers had been killed and scalped. After burying them, Morgan looked in the wagon for any information about their next of kin. It was then that he found the money.

Because of this trust, Trent and Hansen rode from Bannack to Elk City in September. They first contacted Morgan. Then, later, on his recommendation, met with Lloyd and agreed to have him transport their gold, for a modest fee, to Lewiston.

A star, fashioned from iron bars and circled by the metal rim of a wagon wheel, hung from the overhead cross timber of the miners' front gate. Suspended from that was a sign that read, appropriately, "The Lone Star Mine."

"Very fitting," Lloyd said to Charles Allen, as the two men stood their horses in front of the mine gate.

"Texas Rangers, were they?" Charles asked, as he opened the gate for Lloyd and the horses.

"That's what Morgan tells me. I've never talked to them about anything except business. I just met them last year, but they seem like men who know what they are doing."

"Why don't they take the gold to Lewiston by themselves?" Allen asked. "They sure as hell aren't afraid of desperados, being ex-Rangers and all."

"No, I don't think they are afraid of that so much, but if they take their gold out, then they leave their mine abandoned. I guess they figure the boys in Bannack would discover how rich the mine is. Then they would have trouble. They trust me because I'm running for political office," Lloyd said, smiling. "I think the real reason, though, is Lester Morgan. They know he works for me, so that's good enough for them. They all knew each other in Texas."

"Was Morgan a Ranger, too?" Allen asked.

"No, he sold horses to the Rangers and, I guess, he used

to run around a little with these folks, 'cause they are fairly close, it seems," Lloyd said.

Lloyd and Allen walked their horses toward the miners' cabin. He could see a much larger home under construction in the background. Lloyd recognized the three miners, who were sitting on wood chunks around a camp fire, just a few feet from the cabin door. He didn't recognize two younger men standing behind the three seated men.

"Good to see you men again," Lloyd said, grinning, as he shook hands with Hansen, Trent, and Seibel. Turning to Allen, Lloyd said, "This is Charles Allen, my chief packer."

Allen shook hands with the three men, then the younger men, as Seibel introduced them as his nephews, Sam and Jake Calder from Texas. "They rode with the Rangers a spell," Seibel said proudly, as he grinned at his nephews, who were now feeling a little uncomfortable with the sudden attention.

Trent brought two chairs and a pot of coffee from the cabin. After Lloyd and Charles were seated and starting on their coffee, Hansen asked, "You boys have a good trip?"

Charles looked at Lloyd, who spoke. "All except for one little setback. We lost three mules and nearly a man," he continued, as the men looked at him expectantly. Lloyd pointed toward Phillips, who was removing packs and supplies from the mules in a distant meadow. "Phillips down there rode through a wasp nest, set his horse and the mules crazy. They run off a cliff just before you descend down to the Bitterroot on one side and the Little Clearwater on the other. Phillips grabbed a treetop as his horse went over or he would have been a goner too."

"Bet that made his backside pucker some!" Sam Calder spouted.

"Sure did," Lloyd said, remembering how Phillips had wet his pants. "Made mine pucker a little, too," he added, remembering his own close call at the cliff.

The men exchanged small talk for a few minutes. Then Hansen, who was more impatient than the others, suggested that they get down to the business at hand. Seibel started the meeting off. "It's my understanding, Lloyd, that you are going on over to Virginia City, unload your supplies, then return here."

"That's correct," Lloyd said. "When we get back, I'll load your gold and head straight to Lewiston. I'm only going to stop in Elk City overnight. Then I'll head out again. I think I'll take Lester on to Lewiston with me, because I'll have to admit, I'm a little uncomfortable with all this gold. An extra gun along won't hurt."

"Sure won't," Seibel said. "I'll even have Sam and Jake ride along. Both boys are pretty damn good with six-shooter or rifle."

"That's good," Lloyd said. "We can also use more help with the mules. It's pretty damn tough getting a hundred twenty mules over the Bitterroots with three men, even with half the mules unloaded."

All the men nodded in agreement. They had all crossed the Bitterroots.

Trent asked, "Do you think any attention will be paid to you taking dynamite out of the gold fields?"

"No," Lloyd said, "if we meet anyone on the trail or in Elk City who asks about all the dynamite, I'll just tell them that it's bad and we are returning it to the company we bought it from." All the men agreed that sounded reasonable.

"When will you be back here from Virginia City, Lloyd?" Seibel asked.

"Probably around the fourth of October," Lloyd said. "I'm on a schedule and I don't want to fall behind. If a big snow comes, a man might not get out."

"True enough," Hansen said. "A lot of miners are leaving already. Only a few, like us, are staying the winter. Course there is enough supplies in Bannack to get several hundred men through the winter, so it's not too bad."

"Even a few of the finer sex here," Jake Calder said. He was smiling, but when all the men looked at him and returned his smile, Jake colored with embarrassment.

"The boys met a couple of the finer sex over at Skinner's Saloon last night," Seibel said, grinning at his nephews. Sam and Jake looked at each other and the men broke out in laughter.

Sam, eager to change the subject, asked Lloyd if he and Jake would offend anyone by helping Phillips with the mules. Lloyd told him to go ahead and that he appreciated the help. Allen got up and went with the younger men to help.

"How far are we from Bannack?" Lloyd asked Seibel.

"Just over that hill about a quarter mile," he replied.

"You fellows want to ride into town and get a beer?" Lloyd asked.

At that very moment, in a room in back of Skinner's Saloon, four men sat around a table at another meeting. James Romain took the bottle from William Page's hand. "No drinking until after we are through talking. I want everyone in full attention and a sober frame of mind."

Page didn't object, but in his simple, almost retarded way, he looked like a small child, even though he was almost sixty years old.

Romain continued. "Here's the plan. Doug," he said to Lower, "I want you and Billy here to try and join up with the Magruder party as mule skinners."

"Yah, you already told us that, but where do you want us to try at? Didn't you say he was going on over to Virginia City, then come back through here?"

"That's right," Romain said. "When he comes back here, he will have over twenty thousand in gold from selling his supplies. I want you and Billy to offer your services by helping him with the mules."

"We will make our move after they leave Bannack and start back for Elk City. When they cross the Bitterroot, they will almost have to camp on that steep ridge about two miles above the river. That's the only place where they can pasture one hundred twenty some mules and still have a big enough place for a camp."

"A hundred twenty mules!" Lower exclaimed. "I thought he only had sixty or so. Why so many?"

Romain and Renton exchanged glances. Romain continued, "Rumor is that Magruder is starting a freight line. Maybe he is going to have an outfit going both ways over the trail."

"Makes sense to me," Renton said in support of this thought. Lower agreed, but Billy Page didn't say anything. He was too busy looking at the bottle of whiskey setting on the floor next to his chair.

"Anyway," Romain continued, "I want you and Billy to volunteer for guard duty each night. Tell them that it's the least you can do for them letting you go along. Each night that you camp, before you reach the Bitterroot River, I want you to make contact with me on your back trail. Just get into a habit of relieving yourself about ten o'clock each night. When you leave the camp, we will contact you and adjust our plan based on the information you give us.

"On the night they camp at the ridge above the Bitterroot, we will wait until they are asleep. Billy, I want you to shoot Phillips in the head. Just make sure you put your bed roll near his each night, so no one pays attention when you move in close to him, Doug, I want you to hit Allen in the head with an axe before Billy shoots Phillips. Renton and I will use axes on Magruder and the two gunmen who the mine people are sending with the gold."

"What gunmen?" Lower asked.

Romain and Renton looked at each other. Romain realized his mistake. He looked at Billy Page, who was again admiring the whiskey bottle on the floor. "I'll cover that in a minute," he said to Lower, as he nodded his head toward Page.

Lower looked at Page, then back at Romain. He nodded his head as Romain continued.

"We'll take the gold and what personal effects we want, then head straight to Lewiston. We will pass Elk City altogether."

"I'm not a good enough shot to hit Phillips in the head," Page said. The other men looked at Bill Page. Romain wondered how in hell he got stuck with this idiot. He guessed someone said Page knew the mountains well.

"Shoot him in the damn stomach then," Romain said angrily. Page just looked at Romain without expression or comment.

"After we take care of everyone, we'll run the stock off and burn the gear, make it look like Indians. I've got some moccasins we can put on and I'll drop this Indian knife at the camp.

"Once we get to Lewiston, we'll book passage on a riverboat and head to San Francisco. When we get there, we're splitting up and it'll be every man for himself then."

"Where do we divide the gold?" Lower asked.

"Soon as the job is finished, we'll do that. Any more questions?" Romain asked the group. No one had any, so he told Page to ride out to the Lone Star Mine and keep a look out for Magruder's outfit. "Get back here and let me know when he arrives," Romain said. "He's due in today."

"How do you know that?" Lower asked.

"Friend of Cyrus Skinner's got drunk with two nephews of one of the mine owners. He tells me the boys got to braggin' about how Magruder was workin' for them and that they were going to accompany Magruder on his trip back.

"Get going, Billy," Romain ordered. "We need to know where Magruder is at when he gets here."

Billy Page, now halfway attentive to the conversation, nodded his head and left the room.

"Now, what is it that you couldn't say around Page?" Lower asked.

"Didn't want to talk around him," Romain said. "He drinks too much and he might talk if things don't go just right. Besides," Romain continued, "we don't want to cut him in on a quarter million dollars."

"What?" Lower said.

"That's right, quarter million. You see," Romain continued, "when Magruder gets back from Virginia City, he's going to have a lot of gold from selling his supplies, but when he leaves here, he's going to have a lot more than just his own gold. The miners over at the Lone Star apparently hit the Mother Lode and Magruder is going to take it out of here for them."

"How come we haven't heard about their find around here and how come you know about it?" Lower asked.

"There's someone else involved, but let's just say he's a knowledgeable source, when it comes to what Magruder is doing. Anyway, what the plan is, we're gonna kill Magruder and his men, then we're gonna take that gold ore he's haulin' for the Lone Star and bury it. We will use Magruder's gold, which he got out of his supplies, for living expenses, then come back in a year or so and haul the gold out under the pretext that we're freighters. Actually, we are supposed to pack the gold to Granite Springs and bury it there, but the other party who wanted us to do this, is going to be left out of the deal. Renton and I have discussed it and we feel, since we are taking all the risks, he don't need to be included."

"I don't know," Lower said, "I don't like screwing a partner out of a deal, even if I don't know him. I mean, what if he gets upset to the point he turns us in?"

"Don't feel bad about him," Romain said. "He wanted us to kill you and Page after we got the gold to Granite Springs."

Lower's mouth dropped open. "Who is this son-of-a-whore?" he asked.

"His name is John Wick," Romain said, "but it doesn't matter. You are never gonna have the pleasure of meeting the man. When we by pass Elk City, Renton and I are gonna torch Magruder's store, because Mr. Wick lives in the top part of it. He will never have a chance to get out, especially if he's sleeping, which we will make sure of."

"Maybe I should light the match," Lower said thoughtfully. In the same breath, he asked, "but what about Billy? I've kinda got to likin' the old buzzard. I don't want anything to happen to him."

"I don't care if he comes along and does what he's told, but I'm not going to split any gold with him. He wouldn't know what to do with it anyway," Romain said. "We can give him a few hundred, but I want to be miles away from him when he starts drinkin'. Maybe to be safe, poor old Billy might have an accident by falling off the boat between Lewiston and Portland."

Lower didn't have a chance to comment on that, because Billy Page burst through the door. "That Magruder fella, he's here," Page spouted excitedly.

"Well, why aren't you watching him then?" Romain asked angrily.

"'Cause he's here," Page said, "Comin' to this saloon with Mr. Trent, Hansen, and Seibel. There is also some other men that I don't know with them."

The three men jumped from their seats at the table and looked through the wall cracks into the main portion of the saloon. Eight men were seating themselves at two different but adjacent tables.

"Which one is Magruder?" Lower asked.

"The one carryin' that new repeating rifle."

"They say rifles like that shoot fifteen times without reloading," Romain said.

"They have metal cartridges that holds the powder and lead," Renton added.

"Where did you run into them, Billy?" Lower asked.

"I was just getting ready to ride out to the mine, when I saw this group of men standin' around this other fella, who was a-talkin' and handin' out these pieces of paper with things tellin' 'bout him. I went over to listen and several fellars said he was Lloyd Magruder, a businessman and maybe the next governor to the new territory. Anyway, I heard them talkin' 'bout commin' here for beer, so I high-tailed it over here 'fore they did."

"You did good, Billy." Romain said.

After a few moments, Romain said, "Let's get out the back door. Renton and I will go to our cabin. Lower, you and Billy come back in the front door. Maybe you can let it be known that you're headed for Lewiston in a week or so and would like to help Magruder, if he would be so kind to take you with him. Just don't ask him questions that would make him suspicious."

The four men quietly slipped out the back of Skinner's Saloon and disappeared into the night.

13

Murder in the Bitterroots

My Dearest Caroline,
    Although I've been gone but a short time, it truly seems like years. I have been away from you before, have missed you terribly before, but this time seems so different. I don't know why, maybe it's these mountains. They are so vast, so majestic, so . . . so very lonely.

    Lloyd stopped writing. He desperately wanted to write a letter to Caroline, but many of the things he wanted to write about would be a security risk, should the letter fall into the wrong hands. Lloyd rechecked his notes concerning the topics that he wanted to tell Caroline about. He was having a difficult time keeping his mind on the business points he needed to advise her on.
    Really, what he wanted to do, was hold her. He needed to hear her voice, touch her skin, and watch her warm smile. Lloyd could almost picture the scene when he would return to her. He would notice her smile first. Even if she was surrounded by other people, he would be able to pick out her smiling face. Lloyd's attention returned to his notes, as he started underlining the information that he probably should not include in the letter. On the list he marked off: amount of gold; where he was while writing this letter; his expected time of arrival back in Lewiston; the renegade outlaw sheriff, Henry

Plummer; and his own requested nomination at the Democratic Convention for the new Idaho Territory Representative.

In looking back over his list, Lloyd realized that he had excluded everything except his loneliness and love for Caroline. He started to consider again. Erand Michaels was a trustworthy young man. Trent, Hansen, and Seibel recommended him highly, even though he was very young. They assured him Michaels would deliver the letter in a timely and reliable manner. Lloyd started writing again. *To heck with it,* he thought, *I'll put everything in. Sometimes a man can become too afraid.*

Lloyd finished writing, then folded the letter and put it into an envelope. He sealed it with wood pitch and wax, then placed the envelope into his shirt pocket. He left the smaller cabin and walked to the larger, now nearly complete, two-story home the miners had been working on. The men were seated around a large plank table, eating breakfast.

Gary Trent was removing fried potatoes, eggs, and elk steak from the stove. "Don't have as many eggs as I'd like," he said. "Damn weasel got into our chicken pen last week and killed two of our best layers. The others quit layin' for a spell after that."

Lloyd grinned and winked at the Calder brothers. "Guess I'd quit layin', too, if a weasel got after me," Lloyd replied. The Calder brothers returned his grin, as he sat down at the table.

"Mornin', Lloyd," Don Seibel said. "You are ready for the trip?" he asked.

"Seems like I've never stopped being ready," Lloyd replied. "I've been in the saddle steady now for a month and a half. It has been worth it, though. This has been the most rewarding venture I've ever been able to accomplish."

"For us, too," Hansen replied. "We are darn lucky to have run into you. I don't know how else we could have gotten our gold out of here. Course, it may not be so bad around here now that Plummer and his bunch are gone. It's so damn hard to tell who's honest."

"Oh, you boys could have gotten it out," Lloyd replied.

"Yah, but we would have had to leave our mine to do it, and the way it's producing, we couldn't afford to leave it. No telling who would have walked in and just helped themselves," Hansen said.

"Speakin' of trusting folks, Lloyd, can we trust those two men you've hired?" Seibel asked.

"Well, I haven't really hired them, Don. They just asked if they could go with us, because they are out of grub and plan to get out of the mountains for a while. Claim they are returning to Walla Walla. Charles Allen, here, knows a little about them and I've seen them around Lewiston off and on for the last year or so."

"What do you know about them, Charles?" Seibel asked.

"Well, they always seem to be working, or at least tryin' it. Bill Page has done some packin' for the miners in the gold camps, but I don't think he really is smart enough to make money out of it. I hear that he has a place somewhere down on the Columbia, but mostly he just drifts around trying to pick up odd jobs for himself. Like Lloyd says, he's always trying to work. I understand that he and the other fellow are just askin' for grub as their only pay."

"That's correct," Lloyd said. "I'm sure they are okay, but I'll have to admit, I don't know the other fellow."

"Well, we at least have them outnumbered if they are no good," Phillips added.

"Yah, and it's probably better to have them around if they are headed your direction anyway. At least, you can keep an eye on them," Seibel said.

The men were nearly finished with breakfast, when three riders rode in. Lloyd recognized the man in the center as Erand Michaels, the young man why Lloyd had asked to take his letter to Caroline. "Hello, Mr. Magruder," Michaels said, as he dismounted at the front of the cabin.

"Hello, Erand," Lloyd replied. "You fellows on your way?"

"Yes, sir," Michaels said. "And we hope to be in Lewiston in ten days."

"That's damn good time," Allen said.

Looking at him, Michaels said, "Yes, sir, it's about forty-five miles a day."

"Course you boys are travelin' light, with no pack animals, so you can make good time," Seibel said.

"If you want, stop at my ranch in Elk City," Lloyd said. "See Lester Morgan and tell him you're taking a letter for me. He'll put you up for the night and give you some grub."

"I would, Mr. Magruder, but my two friends here like to spend their money in places they shouldn't, so we will probably ride around Elk City."

The two young men sat atop their horses and looked nervous. Either would have shifted his feet, had he been on the ground. "We don't spend our money any more foolish than Sam and Jake," one of them replied. That shifted the attention to the Calder boys, who shot warning scowls at their mounted friends. The older men had a good laugh, while the four younger ones glared at each other. Seibel broke their stare down, when he asked Erand where they were going after they got to Lewiston.

"After I deliver Mr. Magruder's letter, we're going to sell our horses and buy fare on the riverboat to Portland. I hear tell that a shipyard is hiring, so we thought we'd get jobs there. We're not doing so good at this mining business," He added.

Lloyd handed Erand his letter, "You remember who to give this to, don't you?"

"Yes, sir, Mr. Beachy at the Luna House."

"Yes, or his wife," Lloyd added.

Erand mounted, "I'll get it there, Mr. Magruder." Then he spoke to Sam and Jake. "If you fellows get down to Portland, stop by and see us. Maybe we can spend some more foolish money."

Sam and Jake cast nervous glances at their uncle, who pretended not to notice.

The men all waved good-bye, as the three young men turned their horses and rode west. Their intentions were good and their honesty was without question. Sometimes, however, their youth inspired irresponsibility.

The following day, at 4:00 A.M., they had the mules harnessed with pack saddles and loaded with two fifty-pound boxes that displayed the word "Dynamite" in black letters four inches tall. Each box was tightly sealed and fitted with two short ropes fashioned into loops. The men simply placed the loop around one of the forks of the single tree pack, and the process of loading and unloading the gold onto the mules could be done in a matter of minutes by seven men.

William Page and Doug Lower had arrived at the mine the previous evening. Everyone knew Page, except the Calder brothers, but no one had met Lower before. Lloyd and Charles sized up the man, but found no fault with him. His smile and friendly, humorous nature even set the ex-lawmen at ease. That evening, in fact, Hansen and Lower went fishing together at a nearby stream. The fish were biting and by dark the men had caught over seventy rainbow that averaged ten inches in size. The following morning, the men ate a breakfast of fried spuds and trout. Lloyd couldn't remember when he had had a better breakfast.

Don Seibel had a small concern, but he kept it to himself. He felt that it was really none of his business, but three times that morning, he saw Billy Page take several nips from a whiskey flask.

Hansen and Lower had almost become friends. Lower

had told Hansen to look him up if he ever got down on the Columbia. "I'll take you sturgeon fishing," Lower had said. Hansen, ever impatient, was impressed with Lower's efficient, pitch-in, get-it-done attitude, as they harnessed the mules that morning. He even expressed this to Lloyd, who agreed.

"He's a worker, all right," Lloyd had said. "Good man to have on the trail with you."

Lower smiled to himself, when he heard Lloyd's comment. In the early morning darkness, Lloyd and John hadn't noticed the quiet Lower work his way toward them. They hadn't noticed him as he quietly pried one end of a board loose on a dynamite box. He had reached inside and felt what he expected to feel. Gold!

They hadn't noticed him, as their conversation turned to the gold in the dynamite boxes, nor did they see him drift silently away and continue to work with other mule harnesses, while they finished their conversation.

Lower continued to smile. He had always prided himself on his stealth. He loved his ability to perform as people expected, even enjoyed. He loved playing a role, loved the challenge of deceit. He often thought that he should have stayed in the New York theaters. He loved the recognition, the applause, the notoriety. He had loved everything about the theater. Everything, of course, except the money.

That's why he had left New York. Like thousands of others, Lower had been lured to the West by the call of gold. Also, like many others, he found that finding the gold was hard work. This he didn't like. Using his brain was more to his liking. He tried real estate in Portland, but found no challenge in that. After several months, he drifted up the Columbia, sometimes taking jobs on riverboats as a deck hand. Quickly tiring of manual labor, he left the riverboats and took another job at Biggs Ferry, shuttling people who were traveling to the interior of Oregon across the river.

It was here he met William Page. Page had used the ferry to move his cattle across the Columbia. He told Lower that he was going to make some quick, easy money by selling the cattle to miners on the Powder River. Lower liked that thought, so he quit his job as a ferry man. He and Page picked up a few more cattle that seemed to be running free and sold those along with the others.

Later, Lower and Page drifted on over to Walla Walla, where they met Renton and Romain. For the next two months, the four men traveled together, before finally staking claims, under alias names, around the gold camps of Virginia City, Montana. On two occasions Lower had watched while Romain and Renton, deserters from the Union Army, shot dead three miners and robbed them of their gold. Lower hadn't liked the killing, but, he had to admit, it was quick and easy money.

The three men hadn't done their dirty work around Page, because, as Romain put it, "He's always stupid and drunk." Romain and Renton didn't particularly care for Page, but Lower liked him. He found that the aging man could be easily manipulated and used as a tool.

When it came to quick and easy money, Lower could work. Each morning, Lower was the first one up. He would have a fire and coffee going by the time Lloyd got up, and he was loading mules before the rest of the men crawled out of their bed rolls.

It was the fourth evening before Lloyd noticed anything. On that day, Lower, after they had stopped for the evening camp and unloaded the mules, left the camp on their back trail, apparently to make a nature call. That in itself wasn't so strange, but Lloyd and, even Charles, noticed that every time he did that, Page would stand near the camp and stare after Lower until he disappeared in the trees.

"That Page is a strange bird," Charles said. "He stands

and stares after Lower every time he goes for a relief call. He's always a-sippin' on his whiskey flask. You'd think he would be out of whiskey by now."

"He is, but Lower isn't," Lloyd said. "Lower carries a couple bottles in his saddle bag. Saw him filling Page's flask for him yesterday. It's kinda like Page is the steward and Lower is the master, but I guess that's their business."

"I figure it the same way," Allen said. "So long as they do their part, I'll not press 'em. But Page seems to be hitting that flask more in the last couple of days. If'n he gets affected any, I'll have a talk with him. Tomorrow 'bout noon, we'll start into the mountains and timber. We don't want him liquored up in that kind of country."

"That's for damn sure," Lloyd said, remembering his and Phillips' narrow escape.

Three hundred yards down the trail, Lower felt his way carefully in the semi-darkness. He called out softly, but it was the third time before Romain answered. "Here," he said. Lower worked his way to a fir thicket and crawled under the low, thick branches. He could see the dim outline of Romain and Renton.

"Everything going according to plan?" Romain asked.

"Yah, they aren't the least bit suspicious and we will cross the Bitterroot tomorrow. Probably cross the river, then camp on top of that steep ridge a couple miles above the river. Magruder says that's the only spot for miles around that's big enough and flat enough to camp with a hundred mules."

"Do you know the area?" Romain asked.

"No, but Page does. He says they are going to probably camp at a flat bench on the ridge. They'll picket the mules about two hundred yards up the ridge on another flat bench."

"Who's going to be on guard tomorrow night?" Renton asked.

"Probably me and Magruder, after midnight. It'll be Allen

121

and one of the Calder brothers until then."

Romain thought for a moment. "That's good. If the guard arrangement changes, you take your hat off and keep it off. We'll be watching until you can make contact with us, if it does change."

"Okay, fine," Lower said.

Romain continued, "Here's how we'll do it. You will probably have a fire up on the hill with the mules, won't you?"

"Yah, I'm sure. It's too damn cold to not have one."

"Okay then, take an axe up the hill with you to build the fire. Soon as you get a chance, hit Magruder in the head with it. Don't use your gun, because I don't want to alarm the others. I want you to do it an hour after you and Magruder go on watch, so that will be at 1:00 A.M., understand?"

"Yah, I got it. That will give Allen and the Calder boy time enough to get to sleep after we relieve them."

"That's right, and at 1:00 A.M. Renton and I are going to start in the camp. I want you to tell Page to sleep close to Phillips. If there is a commotion, have him shoot Phillips. If he don't have to shoot Phillips, then we'll take care of him last. He's probably the least dangerous to us."

"I hope the Calder boys don't wake up," Lower said. "They are pretty good with six-shooters, especially Jake. I saw him shoot the head off a blue grouse at thirty feet, couple days ago."

"There won't be any slip-ups," Romain said. "If everyone does their part, this will go off without a hitch. Here," he said, "wear these tomorrow and give Page a pair." He handed Lower two pair of moccasins.

A few moments later, Lower slipped from under the tree and made his way back to the camp. He had pulled his shirt tail out of his pants and was tucking it back as he walked into camp.

With all of the day's chores done, Lower crawled into his

bed roll. He was exhausted from all the unaccustomed work. Page spread his bed roll on the other side of the campfire from Lower. He appeared to be in deep thought as he removed his flask from his hip pocket. He was looking at Lower as he drank deep from the bottle. The whiskey burnt his throat, but it also chased away the fear and anxiety that hounded him. The fire felt good in these high lonely mountains.

Lower was up before first light that morning. The high-pitched bugle of a bull elk had awakened him. He had stoked up the fire and was preparing to start loading the mules when Sam Calder climbed out of his bed roll. "Morning, Doug," he said. "You cookin' breakfast?"

Lower grinned. "You cook and I'll do the dishes," he returned.

The bull bugled again and both men looked in the direction of his squeal. Moments later, another bull took up the challenge. "Wish we had more time, I would like to go after one of those fellas," Sam said.

Lower grunted an agreement, then walked over and kicked Page on the bottom of his foot. "Get up, Billy, we got work to do."

William Page groaned as he rolled over and finally raised himself up on one elbow. He removed his flask from under his saddle and took a long pull. As he sat the bottle down, tears welled up in his eyes as he fought the desire to cough. The whiskey brought Page around and he got out of his bed roll, as Phillips and Jake Calder came in from their morning mule guard.

Sam Calder positioned a grill over the fire for frying bacon and started boiling water for coffee.

Lloyd and the others started loading the dynamite boxes on the mules. Every man went about his chores without direction or comment. By five-thirty the men and mules were ready to start down the trail.

The only pause in the morning routine came when Page asked Lloyd what was wrong with the dynamite they were taking back to Lewiston. "Half of it don't go off," he answered, "so we are going to try and get a new batch." That satisfied Page's curiosity and no more questions were asked, but Lower didn't miss the exchange of glances between Lloyd and the Calder boys.

Lloyd pulled his silver watch and opened it. Caroline's picture stared at him. "It's 5:35, boys. We'd better hit the saddle." Just then, the elk bugled again, but this time he was answered by a half-dozen mules. Charles Allen grinned as he mounted his horse and led the pack string out of camp. The bull elk was really getting pissed at the mules.

The morning was beautiful in the Bitterroots and the higher the men climbed, the father they could see. Lloyd noticed that the higher peaks had taken on snow during the night. He knew it wouldn't be long before the trail over the Bitterroots would be closed until the following spring. In fact, he suspected his pack string would probably be the last travelers over the South Nez Perce Trail this fall, unless there were some miners coming directly behind him on their way to milder winter grounds.

As they climbed higher, the air became colder and the men put their coats on. At noon a light snow began to fall, but the scenery was so magnificent that the men scarcely noticed. Many rugged mountains of granite thrust their needle-like peaks into the sky, while their adjacent neighbor was covered with a green carpet of pine and spruce.

Lloyd saw an eagle soaring overhead and reined his horse in to watch it. He was surprised at the emotion it produced in him. Freedom, independence, loneliness, and courage echoed from the eagle as it soared high overhead. As he watched the mighty bird in its graceful circle, a song came to his mind that blended with his surroundings and the eagle.

It was called "Away to the Mountains," and he sang it softly as he nudged his horse and moved along with the pack train.

By four o'clock that afternoon, the pack train came within view of the Bitterroot. Looking far below, the river looked like a thin blue ribbon, as it snaked its way down the valley floor.

"How far to the river?" Lower asked Allen.

"Oh, probably two miles. Then once we get to the river, we got another two miles straight up before we get to those flat benches where we can camp. We're probably looking at another two hours before we pitch camp. We have to water the stock, too, once we get to the river."

The next two hours went quickly, even though the terrain was steep. By six-thirty, the pack train arrived at the flat benches of a steep mountain ridge, two miles above the Bitterroot. They had now passed the halfway point between Bannack and Elk City. The snow flurry had turned into a misty rain, so Charles Allen and Sam Clader pitched a tent, while Lloyd and the other men took the mules to the upper bench. There, they put out picket lines and tied the mules and horses.

"Good grass here for the stock," Phillips said, as they finished tying the last mule.

"Yah, but this whole hillside will be ate down to bare ground in the morning," Lloyd said.

As he and Phillips started back down the hill to the camp, Lloyd noticed Page and Lower at the far end of the clearing. The men were standing close and speaking in low voices. "Those two men are up to something," Lloyd said. "Every once in a while, I see them talking secret-like."

"I've noticed it, too," Jake Calder said, coming up behind Phillips and Magruder.

"I think we better keep an eye on them and I think we better keep them apart, so they don't stand any guard duty together," Lloyd said. The three men walked on down the hill, where Charles and Sam had a roaring fire going. A pot of pork and beans was on the cooking grill.

Lloyd told Charles and Sam about his suspicion of Lower and Page. "Charles, Lower and I are going to relieve you and Sam tonight. Do you suppose someone ought to keep an eye on Page? If they keep acting this way, I'm going to have a talk with them," Lloyd said. "Maybe I will anyway."

"Let's just watch 'em a little more," Phillips said. "Page usually throws his bed roll close to mine, so I can keep an eye on him. I sleep light anyway."

That satisfied Lloyd, so the men dropped the subject and started dishing up their dinner from the grill pot.

Up on the upper bench, Lower was going over the plan with Page a second time.

"I . . . I don't think I can shoot straight enough to hit Phillips in the head," Page insisted.

"Do like Romain says then, shoot him in the damn guts," Lower hissed.

"Kinda like Phillips," Page said, as he took a long drink from his flask.

"I don't give a damn who you like, Billy. Just do it if he wakes up, Okay?"

"Yah, I guess," Page replied.

"Come on, Billy, let's get down to the camp. Magruder was looking at us a while ago."

Lloyd had barely got to sleep, when Charles Allen shook him awake. "It's midnight, Lloyd," he said.

"Okay, Charles. You wake Lower yet?"

"Yah. He started up the hill already, 'cause I told him the fire was dying down."

Lloyd nodded as he crawled out of his bed roll and put his boots on. "See you in a few hours," he said, as he ducked out of the tent. Charles barely heard Lloyd, as he lay down and went to sleep within several moments.

Page watched Lloyd start up the hill through the slits of his eyelids, as he feigned sleep. William Phillips snored deeply three feet from his bed roll. Page's heart raced. The next hour would be the longest wait of his life. His heart nearly stopped, when he saw Lloyd halt at the foot of the hill, turn, and look at him. He could see that Lloyd was carrying his .44 Morse repeater. He could see the gold name plate on the rifle stock and wondered what it said. After a few moments, Lloyd turned and went on up the hill.

Page didn't move, but he did open his eyes. He was pretty sure that Allen had already fallen asleep, but he wasn't sure about Sam Calder. His only hope was that Phillips wouldn't wake up.

Page eased the flask from his pocket and took several long drinks. He liked the burning sensation as the whiskey went down his throat. Hell, he might even be able to shoot Phillips, if he had to.

In the distant shadows, just out of the fire light, two shadowy figures skirted the camp and approached the tent that Charles was sleeping in.

Up on the upper bench, with the mules, Lower was chopping branches from a dead log and throwing them to Lloyd, who was stacking them for the night supply.

"What's the date today, Lloyd?" Lower asked.

"Sunday, October 11th."

Lower paused in his chopping and walked toward Lloyd, whose back was to him. Lloyd was bent over the fire, lighting his pipe, which he smoked only on rare occasions.

"What time is it?" Lower asked.

Lloyd pulled out his silver watch and flipped it open. Caroline's picture stared at him. "One-o-one A.M.," Lloyd said.

"That's close enough," Lower said and sank the head of his axe through Lloyd's spine at the top of his shoulders. Lloyd fell sideways, the axe still embedded in his back. He couldn't understand it, he could see his left hand in the fire, but he couldn't move it, couldn't pull away. It didn't matter, though, it didn't hurt. He wondered why he could see his skin start to blister. He saw Lower reach toward him, then he died.

Romain and Renton walked from the shadows. Each man carried an axe. They approached the Calder brothers, who were sleeping side by side. They raised the axes together and each man hit a Calder boy at the same time. Jake moaned and rolled over before he died. Sam died instantly.

"What should we do about Allen?" Renton asked. "He's sleeping in a damn tent. Can't hit him with an axe."

"I can hit him with this," and Romain pulled his .44 Colt. "You take care of Phillips, I'll get Allen."

Romain walked to the tent, opened the flap, and put the muzzle against Allen's head. The shot was muffled, but it blew chunks of Allen's head all over the tent wall.

Renton wasn't close enough to Phillips when he sat up in his bed roll. Page pulled his pistol, cocked it, and shot Phillips in the stomach. Phillips rolled over screaming in pain. "You murdering son of a bitch." He pulled his own Colt and fired at Renton, who was running toward him with the axe raised. The slug grazed Renton's ribs, but did little more than burn his skin. Renton sank the axe to the hilt in Phillips's forehead. He fell and died instantly.

For several moments, the only sound that could be heard was the crackling of the fire. The four bandits, now murderers, stood in the center of a bloody camp. The flickering fire light danced across Romain's face. His eyes were bugged and a smile started on his face. The instant viewer would have described him as satanic in appearance.

Page was still on his knees looking at Phillips, his gun arm raised with the revolver still pointing at the dead man. A low moan turned into a wail, starting in the bowels of his stomach. His hand started shaking and the revolver fell from his grip.

Doug Lower was walking down the hill from the upper flat. He was carrying Magruder's rifle. David Renton was examining the flesh wound across his ribs.

Off in the distance, a coyote made a mournful howl of protest at the brutality in the Bitterroots.

14

Wick Quits

John Wick didn't want to ask her for the letter. He knew she wouldn't give it to him. He knew she liked Magruder and didn't like him. *Damn,* he hated her, hated that young miner who gave her the letter from Magruder, instead of him. That stupid kid should have given him the letter. He's Magruder's partner, or was, he thought. Magruder should be dead by now and must be, or he would have been back.

Wick was outraged. The letter from Magruder was the only communication or sign from the Magruder party. The increasing thought that Romain and Renton had double-crossed him, caused his mind to burn with hate.

Wick had to do something or he would just start shooting people. He had to vent his rage, had to see it and direct it. He had to write. His pace quickened as he left Maxwell's and proceeded past Maggie's, through the foot-deep snow. Rosey Sinclair yelled out the window as he passed, "Wanna come in for something warm, Mr. Wick?" she asked.

He ignored her. *I'll give the bitch something warm,* he thought. Tucking his chin further into his coat and pulling his collar around his neck, he walked in the cold until he got to the store. He went inside, then upstairs to his living quarters. He removed the journal from the chest and began to write.

Friday, October 30th, 1863

The fact that neither Romain or Magruder has showed up is unsettling. Either Renton and Romain have double crossed me, or the whole Damn bunch has shot each other up. Either way, it's happened again. Other people destroying my future. I think it's time I destroyed a few futures.

I left Sarah Maxwell's this morning. Hearing that she got a letter from Magruder, I visited her. She said that a young miner, who was going to deliver the letter to Lloyd's wife in Lewiston, changed his mind and decided to try the new gold fields on the Salmon River. He gave her the letter for someone to deliver.

The stupid idiot anyway, why in hell didn't he leave the letter here. After all, I am Magruder's partner.

Now, I don't know what to do. Probably, I'd better leave here. No telling what's happened and if Romain talks, well, anything could happen . . .

I'll give it a few more days, maybe I can learn something. If not, I'm heading for San Francisco or maybe even back to New York.

There shouldn't be any inquiry about Lester Morgan. I've told people that his leg became bad, that he was in a lot of pain, so he moved to Portland to get some doctorin'. People will believe that. I'll tell them that I'm running the ranch as well.

Sarah Maxwell didn't like John Wick and there was no way she would give him the letter Lloyd had sent to Caroline by Erand Michaels. Maybe she could give it to some miners who were going to Lewiston for the winter, but she didn't really like that idea because she didn't know who to trust since Lester Morgan moved.

Strange, she thought, as she was thinking of him, *that he would move and not come by and say good-bye.*

Sarah wished her father was here, but he had gone to the new gold fields in Florence, with many of the other men. Now she was stuck here, running the barns and taking care of the stock.

Sarah wouldn't take the letter to Lloyd's ranch. She saw John Wick going to and from there. In her dilemma, she finally stuck it behind the mirror in her vanity. It would be many years before she would remove it and read the contents.

Three weeks later, a man from Lewiston arrived in Elk City. He claimed he was a marshall in Lewiston and that Lloyd Magruder and his men had been murdered, robbed, and left in the mountains. The marshall said that they had four men locked up and awaiting trial. He wanted to know if anyone in Elk City knew anything about the situation. Sarah heard that he talked to one miner who saw Lloyd and the others on the trail. The marshall also wanted to know where John Wick was, as Mrs. Magruder wanted the store records. She was going to sell the store and ranch.

While obtaining the books and other mementos from the store, the marshall found John Wick's letter of resignation. It was addressed and written to Lloyd Magruder. It simply said that due to Lloyd's inability to communicate and otherwise assist him in the necessary aspects of running the store, that he was terminating his partnership with Lloyd. The letter went on to complain that since Lester Morgan quit, he was unable to run both the store and ranch. Wick had closed, saying that he had sold the remaining mules and had kept the money for the pay that was due him.

Under the circumstances, the marshall could hardly blame Wick for leaving. The resignation was dated October 31, 1863.

At Magruder's ranch, the marshall found another letter. This letter was to Lloyd and signed by Lester Morgan. It read:

October 11th, 1863

Dear Lloyd,

I am sorry that I have to leave before you return, but it's

132

a case of have to. Each week the pain in my leg increases and it's got to the point that I am now in constant pain. Therefore, I have decided to leave and seek a Doctor that I heard about in San Francisco. Again, please forgive the abruptness in my departure, but it is essential. I have entrusted the ranch and stock into the care of your partner, John wick, until your return.

Lester Morgan

The marshall saw no value in the letter, since Lloyd Magruder would not need the information. He used it in Lloyd's stove that evening to start the fire for cooking his supper on.

Lester Morgan's brother and two sisters in Texas knew that he could not write anything but his own name. The only other person who knew that was Lloyd Magruder.

Several months later, rumor started that was to pass from generation to generation and descendant to descendant. It's birth began one night at Toby's Saloon. Erand Michaels was very drunk. This particular evening, some of the miners were discussing the possibility of Magruder's murderers hiding his gold, since it was believed that very little of the gold had been recovered from the desperadoes upon their capture. Michaels, who was feeling important because he was the center of attention, boasted that Magruder had confided in him that he was hauling thousands of dollars in gold. And, further that he had sent Michaels out to get an armed escort of men from Elk City to meet him on the trail, as Magruder was suspicious of being followed. Michaels went on to tell that he himself had seen Magruder's gold and had wanted to stay and ride with Magruder, but Magruder insisted he ride ahead for help.

Michaels later denied telling this story, but some of the miners in Toby's Saloon that night never heard this denial.

Michaels never did mention that he carried Lloyd's letter, but didn't deliver it as promised. Irresponsibility was not the desired mark of a man in the mining camps.

Sarah Maxwell didn't tell anyone about Lloyd's letter. She figured it was no one's business but Lloyd's next of kin. She would deliver the letter herself when she went to Lewiston in the summer.

On November 28th, a premature dynamite blast collapsed a tunnel, killing five miners. The miners around Bannack City left the men buried in their natural grave. It was bad luck to open the grave of the dead. Besides, the Lone Star mine never did produce any gold. It was a waste of a man's time to reopen it when there were so many other mines that were productive.

15

Janet's Revenge

John Wick sat at his desk, mostly undisturbed. Only occasionally did the tug whistles and the voices of the dock workers interrupt his concentration.

His job as warehouse clerk for San Francisco's largest shipping company provided him with ample time for his journal writing. Mostly, that's all John Wick did in his spare or social time. He had no friends and only a few acquaintances. He had become withdrawn and depressed. Even more so lately, since the doctor had told him the bad news about the growth that was becoming larger under his right armpit. The pain hadn't been bad at first, but now it was getting to the point that he couldn't hold his arm in its natural position. The pressure against his armpit was almost unbearable.

John Wick was a dying man, and he knew it. The only thing positive in his life was that he would soon be a father. Even that he wasn't sure about. He still hated Janet for funning off with Buck Welch and taking his money.

He had been fortunate running into Janet six months ago at the fish market on Boardwalk Street. He recalled that day with pleasure, as he set his pen down and stared out the warehouse window at the busy San Francisco Bay. Janet had been alone. Her back was to him as she purchased a filet of cod at the open market. After receiving the wrapped fish, she had turned around and nearly bumped into him.

Her face had gone white, then to ashen as he grinned down at her. Janet had cooperated fully when he threatened her with arrest for theft. Wick had simply escorted her to her own apartment. He remembered pulling his pistol with the full intention of shooting her lover. He remembered the extreme disappointment he had felt when Janet told him that Welch had left her, taking most of his money.

Wick had become enraged. He had beat, striped, and raped her. Now she was fully under his power again. If he spoke, she jumped. She was now his slave. *Blackmail and fear work wonders,* he thought.

Janet's baby from Welch had died at birth, so he couldn't extract that revenge. He would, though, make her pay for what she had done to him. She would, in fact, earn his money back, he told her. "Soon as the baby is born, you'll start earning your keep, flat on your back, until you've paid me the seven thousand you stole."

Janet was terrified at this thought. She knew Wick would force her into this service soon after the baby arrived. She must escape, but how? If she left, he would contact the authorities and have her arrested. Prison would be almost as bad as prostitution. Maybe something would intervene. Maybe the cancer would kill Wick before the baby was born. Maybe she would help the cancer along. Then and only then would she be free of this man's evil. Janet was thinking how much she hated this man, who was her husband, hated, despised, and feared him. She wondered what would happen if she simply purchased a fare on the next ship heading for Portland. Just then, Janet realized that John Wick was no longer staring out the window. He was looking intently at her. Her heart seemed to jump into her throat as his gaze pierced her.

"What the hell you thinking about, woman?" he screamed.

"No . . . nothing, John, except . . . that . . . that I'm out of buttons for your shirt that you wanted to wear tomorrow."

"Why 'n hell don't you say so then?" he said, "instead of staring at me. I don't like your damn staring, you hear?"

"Yes . . . yes, John. I do. I'm sorry."

John Wick stared at his wife several moments, then said, "We'll pick some buttons up on the way home tonight. Now hurry up and finish filing those inventory forms."

Wick picked his pen back up and resumed writing in his journal.

Damn good thing they let me bring her to work, he thought. *If they didn't, she would probably run off again. Besides, I get a lot of work done with her here that they don't have to pay for. Probably why Johnson allows it,* Wick mused.

That evening Janet and John walked the several short blocks back to Janet's apartment. They made two stops, one at the fish market and one at a seamstress shop, where Janet purchased several unneeded buttons. Soon after they arrived at her apartment, Wick ordered her to start some dinner.

He, almost immediately, resumed writing in his journal. Janet hated the journal almost as much as she did her husband. She knew he described everything he had done to her and everything that he would do to her in it.

"Get me my laudanum," he ordered. "Then bring me a bucket of beer." Janet went to the pantry and removed a small keg of beer, a cup, and the bottle of laudanum. When she handed them to John, he filled the cup with beer, then poured four drops from the laudanum bottle into the cool beer. "Put the keg back in the pantry," he ordered. "I'm going to get drunk tonight and I don't want to do it on warm beer. Take this, too," he ordered and handed her the bottle of laudanum.

As Janet turned to go back to the kitchen, Wick kicked out, the toe of his boot striking her on the tailbone. The force of the blow propelled her into the wall. Janet slid down the wall, holding her buttocks. Tears of pain and humiliation filled her eyes.

"Move your ass, bitch," Wick yelled, as she struggled to her feet. "Get the hell in there and get my dinner." Janet returned to the kitchen and replaced the beer and laudanum in the pantry.

Painfully and with effort, she started a fire in the cook stove. She prayed that she wouldn't miscarry. The pain in her abdomen hurt as bad as the bruise on her buttocks. Janet put on pans of leftover tomatoes and potatoes to heat up, while she prepared the fish. Tears of pain, and now anger, rolled down her cheeks.

She would no longer take this abuse. He might kill her, but today would be the last day with this monster, she thought.

The dinner was nearly cooked when John Wick called out. "Janet, bring me some more beer and the laudanum, too. This pain is killing me."

I wish it would, she thought. Opening the pantry door, she grabbed the beer and laudanum. Suddenly, she stopped, considered, then started toward the living room again. She stopped again and poured the entire bottle of laudanum into the beer. She took the laudanum bottle to the water bucket and filled it with water. *He won't know the different,* she thought. *They are both clear.*

She put the cork back on the laudanum bottle, then returned to the living room, where she gave them to Wick. He poured four drops into his cup, then filled it with beer. After taking the bottle of laudanum back, Janet started back toward the kitchen.

"Hold it, bitch," Wick ordered. He drank the cup of beer in several gulps, then ordered Janet to refill it. She did, and he allowed her to return to the kitchen.

Janet dished up a plate of food and ate it, alone and in silence. There were no tears, but a look of anxiety crept into her face. She waited fifteen minutes and started to call out, but waited. She waited another fifteen minutes, then called, "John. . . . John, your dinner is ready."

There was no answer, so she waited another five minutes. Then, slowly she opened the kitchen door. John was sitting in a chair. His back was toward her. She noticed that his cup of beer was empty and sitting on the floor beside his chair. His hand was resting on the floor beside the cup. Janet walked to the front of Wick's chair. His journal was open and lying on his lap. John Wick appeared to be asleep.

Janet nudged his foot with her toe. There was no response, so she kicked him in the calf. Still no response. Janet started smiling as tears rolled down her face. She bent down and picked both of his legs up by his ankles. He didn't move, so she pulled him out of the chair. John Wick landed on his back. She dropped his legs on the floor where they remained motionless and spread-eagled. Janet looked at him for a few moments, then suddenly and violently kicked him in the groin. Once, twice, then three times she kicked him. Wick didn't move, but a low moan escaped his lips.

Janet went into the bedroom and got a large pillow. She placed it over his face and held it there a long time. When she removed it, John Wick was dead.

Tears of relief streamed down her face as she walked to a neighbor's and asked them to summon the police.

She answered the few routine questions like a grieving, shocked widow, before the polite constable.

A few days later, Janet Wick booked passage on a steamer bound for Portland. She wanted to find a small home and have it ready when Buck Welch returned from the gold camps. She took with her a few meager personal possessions and clothing. She also took John Wick's journal. If her son or daughter ever wanted to know about their father, she would simply let the child read about him.

16

The Interview

Jerry Rotin and Tom Haugstad grinned back at Marty Kincade from where they were sitting at the front of his desk. "Why can't I stay and get my picture taken with you and Tom?" Rotin asked, in a mock pout.

"Your ugly mug would distract from the story's interest," Marty Kincade replied in friendly banter.

"When's that reporter going to be here, boss?" Haugstad asked, looking at his watch.

"Ten o'clock is what he said," Kincade replied, looking at his own watch.

"That's in five minutes," Rotin said.

"Yah, I know. You better get your gear ready and get going so I can get this guy in and out of here. I've got work to do, too," Kincade replied.

"Well, is Tom going with me or do I have to do this investigation by myself?" Rotin asked.

"No, Tom is going with you, just as soon as the reporter takes our picture. I can answer any questions he asks."

"You mean I don't get to make any famous quotes in the paper?" Haugstad said.

"You have to be famous before your quotes are famous," Kincade said, grinning. He always amused himself with the banter between his detectives. "All you are is infamous and

140

nobody cares about someone like that," he continued.

"Tom, I'll pick you up downstairs in twenty-five minutes," Rotin said as he stood up. "I'm going to get the car serviced and our gear loaded. You should be done brown-nosing and posing with the boss for pictures by then."

Tom winked at Marty, then looked up at his huge partner. "You're just jealous that you didn't get in on the adventure."

"Yah, right," Rotin said, as he left the office grinning. After descending the three floors from Kincade's Investigations, Rotin noticed a small, thin man, wearing round "John Lennon" type glasses. *The nerd reporter,* he thought, as he watched the man studying the Village Mall floor directory. "It's on the third floor, Suite 324," Rotin said, as he walked by the reporter and out the front door of the building.

The thin man stared at the huge detective for several moments before he continued reading the floor directory. Finally he found "Kincade Investigations, Suite 324." The reporter looked back at the front door where Rotin had exited. "How in hell did he know where I was going?" he said to himself, in minor irritation. Sidney Ratsow was a bright man, a real stickler for details, and it irritated him tremendously if he wasn't able to ascertain answers to the many questions that continuously flowed through his mind. He was still brooding over the huge man providing him directions to Kincade's office when he knocked on the door.

Sidney Ratsow momentarily forgot his irritation as Tom Haugstad invited him into the suite. Ratsow was surprised. He had never been in a private detective's office before and his impression of what this office would look like was way off. Ratsow speculated that he would find a dimly lit, dusty office, with old, in need of repair furniture sitting around. Instead, he found a well-lit office with comfortable furniture. Several pictures of wildlife and mountain scenes decorated the walls.

A large painting of Custer, as his last stand, hung on the wall above Kincade's desk. *Not at all like Sam Spade's office,* Ratsow thought.

Marty Kincade stood and introduced himself and then Haugstad. After several moments of small talk, Kincade explained that Haugstad was going to leave for a field investigation and that if Ratsow needed any photographs, he should take them before the interview began. Ratsow nodded and quickly prepared his camera equipment.

In several moments, Ratsow had posed the detectives and snapped several photographs. Haugstad saw Kincade look at him, then his watch. *Damn!* he thought. He was hoping Ratsow would at least ask him one question before he left. "Well, I'm out of here," Haugstad said, as he stood and pointedly faced the reporter. "Nice to meet you, Mr. Ratsow," Haugstad said, smiling and glancing at his boss. "See you around, Mr. Ratsow," Haugstad said, as he thrust out his hand to the reporter, who was now removing a tape recorder from his briefcase. Ratsow gave Haugstad's hand a quick shake, then resumed a hurried activity with his equipment.

Haugstad smiled at Kincade, shrugged his shoulders, and left the office. *What a ham,* Kincade thought as Haugstad closed the door behind himself.

"Well, I'm ready if you are," Ratsow said, looking up from his tape recorder, to Kincade.

"Where do you want me to start?" Marty asked, as he sat behind his desk and faced Ratsow, who had already seated himself.

"Well, to start with, I would like to get a background on you. Then how and why you got involved with a murder case that's nearly 130 years old. Next, I would like to ask you about what happened to the outlaws after the murders. I'm already somewhat familiar with the Magruder murders and what happened prior to the killing, but my research hasn't gone beyond that, as yet. Next, I would like to ask you about the artifacts you found at the murder site and then, if you will, tell me anything about any hidden gold you may have heard about.

"I also understand that the Forest Service is now involved in your find."

"That's correct," Kincade said. "They took the artifacts from me."

"Okay, then," Ratsow said, as he turned the tape recorder on. "Tell me about yourself. Start with your experience as an investigator, but first let me identify and date this interview. Today's date is August 14th, 1992. This is the interview of Marty Kincade, private investigator, at his office in Lewiston. Interview concerns Mr. Kincade's finding of artifacts relating to the Lloyd Magruder murder case of 1863.

"Okay, Mr. Kincade. Go ahead and start with your background. I may stop you here and there with a question."

Marty hesitated a moment, took a deep breath, and started. "I first started in law enforcement in 1969, when I took a job with the campus police at a small college near Seattle. After getting a degree in criminal justice, I started with the Seattle Police Department. After a few years, I made detective and was transferred to a drug task force, working undercover for the Federal Drug Enforcement Administration. After a year of that, I tired of the city and took a job here in Lewiston as a police officer. I continued to work here undercover and that was probably a mistake."

"Why is that?" Ratsow asked.

"Well, by the time I left the Drug Enforcement Administration, I was starting to drink fairly heavy. When I got over here, I was working undercover alone. I had no backup and no partner. I wasn't even allowed to talk with the other officers on the force because they didn't even know I was a cop undercover. The only ones who knew anything were the chief of police and the detective lieutenant. I met with him once a week to turn over drugs that I had purchased and to get more buy money. I felt more like an informant than an undercover officer.

"Anyway, I became more depressed and started drinking more. I suppose I had better watch what I say," Marty said, laughing. "I'm talking to a reporter, not a counselor."

"I won't print anything you don't want me to," Ratsow said. "And you can read my article before it goes to press."

"Fair enough," Marty said, then continued. "After a few years with the Lewiston police force, my grandfather died. We were very close and he was the one who first told me about Lloyd Magruder and started my interest about the circumstances and details surrounding his murder. Also, during this period of time, my wife and I were having marital problems. My drinking had increased and that led to my resignation from the force. I had become involved in a fist fight off duty and, as you probably know, that made a lot of press for a few weeks."

"Yes, I have heard about it," Ratsow said, "but I wasn't a reporter at that time."

"Well, anyway," Marty continued, "after the fight, I was assigned to desk and jail duty. I was told I would be doing that for a long time, as I was a political hot potato. City and county officials wanted me off the street. Some of them even wanted me off the force. I'm telling you all of this because I want you to have my version. I'm quite sure you will hear other people's versions. Anyway, while I was doing jail duty, a woman whom I knew and was very close to, was murdered by her husband. With Grandpa dying, the fight, the press coverage, the murder, and a failing marriage, I was fed up, tired, and depressed. I quit law enforcement and started my own business as a private investigator."

"Okay, so eleven years after you become a private investigator, you work on a murder case that's 129 years old. Surely there was no client who hired you for this," Ratsow said.

"No client hired me," Marty replied. "Like I told you, my grandfather first sparked my interest about Lloyd Magruder's murder when I was a kid. Since then, I've done a lot of reading on the subject and some research of the trial transcripts."

"You mean the trial of Magruder's murderers?" Ratsow asked.

"Yes. And I've also interviewed some very old people, whose ancestors were around Elk City when Magruder was killed."

"What did they tell you?" Ratsow asked.

"Nothing of any real importance," Marty replied. "Mainly just hearsay information that's been passed down over the last hundred years."

"Was there any information about gold being hidden by the bandits?" Ratsow asked.

Marty paused and swallowed before he answered, and Ratsow's interest level increased.

"Yes, of course," Marty replied, smiling, seeing the reporter notice his hesitation. "Aren't there always the romantic, hidden treasure legends that accompany stories like this?" Marty said.

Ratsow looked at Marty's face, searching for signs of deception. After deciding that there was none, he looked at his recorder, then back to his notes. "Okay, so tell me why you traveled two hundred miles from Lewiston into the mountains just to find a few pieces of metal artifacts. I mean it's not like it was a real historical site or anything. Most historical books don't even mention Lloyd Magruder."

Marty looked at Ratsow a few moments. "There are several reasons why I'm interested and why I traveled to the murder scene, but I'm not sure I can explain them so that you can understand."

"Try me," Ratsow stated.

Marty paused again. "Okay, I won't deny that in the back of my mind I was intrigued by the thought of hidden gold. However, after I learned more about the incident, the more I wanted to set the record straight. It was like I wanted to do something for Lloyd Magruder. It is like the whole story was never told and I wanted to finish telling it."

"How so?" Ratsow asked.

"Well, many people thought, and still do, that Lloyd Magruder was not killed in the Bitterroots. Many people believed that he was robbed and killed by the Plummer gang and others believe that he simply just rode away with his gold to start another life."

"And what do you believe?" Ratsow asked.

"I believe that the testimony of William Page is fairly accurate," Marty said. "I believe that for several reasons. First of all, Page testified where the murders happened and what they did to hid the remains of the Magruder party, and all of this was corroborated by Hill Beachy's search party the following spring of 1864. Before Hill Beachy and his searchers left the site, they put up a sign, marking the murder site in memory of the slain men, That sign is now in a museum, here in Lewiston."

"But what corroborating evidence did Hill Beachy's party find?" Ratsow asked.

"They found a human skull and clothing identified as Lloyd Magruder's. They found other human bones on the hillside, below the murder site, where William Page testified they had rolled the bodies. They found a sack full of metal pieces, such as harness and belt buckles, tacks, nails and whatever else that wouldn't burn. These articles, according to Page, were taken from where the outlaws had burned everything and placed in a gunny sack. Page testified that one of the outlaws ordered him to gather up those metal pieces and hide them under a log. He also testified that he did this and it's recorded that he led Hill Beachy to this sack the following spring when he took the search party back."

Ratsow studied his palms. "Well, you know they were not very accurate with description and detail in those days," he finally said.

"Maybe so," Marty replied, "but I know this. I know that I found charcoal eight inches underground, and mixed in with that charcoal, was some lead balls, square nails, harness tacks, and part of what I suspect was a top plate on a surveyor's tripod. This spot was obviously where a man-made fire had been because there was also a circle of rocks around it. Some of the rocks, two or three maybe, protruded through the top of the ground. Tom Haugstad and I found this burn site with a metal detector, exactly thirteen paces from a tree displaying a Forest Service sign, marking this area as the Magruder murder site."

"This is the same location that William Page brought the search party to, so I would say that we have corroborated Page's testimony, for this day and age, wouldn't you, Mr. Ratsow?" Marty said.

Ratsow thought in silence for a while, then said, "Appears so, Mr. Kincade, but like I said earlier, I'm not real familiar with the events that took place after the murders. Could you reflect on that a little?"

"Well, Page's testimony and the newspaper articles give a fairly complete account of those details," Marty said.

"Go on," Ratsow said, after Marty's pause.

"After Magruder and his men had been killed, Renton and Romain ordered Page to go up the hill where the mules were pastured. This was probably done so Renton, Romain, and Lower could divide most of the gold and give Page a much smaller share. I say this because when Page came back from the mules, carrying the harness and other equipment, they told him there wasn't as much gold as they thought. Page testified to that at the trial.

"According to Page, they sent him up the hill to get all of the tack and other equipment. That's probably part of the reason, but I'm sure they wanted to get the gold divided up without Page being there.

"Anyway, when Page returned, they put everything in a pile on the camp fire and burnt it. They wrapped the bodies in a tent, then laid them on a flat rock near the campsite. They pushed the bodies over the hill, which is nearly straight up and down, and let the wolves take care of the rest. Apparently, everything didn't burn up because miners and men of the region reported nearly thirty years later that pieces of harness and pack saddles, along with the bleached bones of the mules, could be seen near the campsite."

"Why the mule bones?" Ratsow asked.

"Well, Page testified that they shot many of the mules near the campsite and also shot them at different times along the trail because the mules followed them. After taking everything they wanted, they finished crossing the Bitterroots and then rode on to Lewiston. When they got to Lewiston, Hill Beachy recognized Magruder's horse, which was ridden by one of the outlaws. That made him suspicious, so he started an investigation and found a rifle in their possession that he had given to Lloyd."

"Hill Beachy swore out warrants for their arrest and William Page confessed, telling the details of the murder to spare his own life. That next March, they hung Renton, Romain, and Lower at a gallows constructed at what is now a parking lot of a grocery store. That was Idaho's first murder trial and first legal hanging."

"Very interesting. What happened to the gold they took from Magruder?"

"History differs in the amount recovered," Marty said, "but it's believed that Caroline Magruder received about ten thousand in gold from Hill Beachy after he arrested the outlaws."

Ratsow sat in thought several moments, then asked Marty what the Forest Service had done with the artifacts he had found.

"Last I heard, they were going to be placed at the University of Idaho, but I don't know if they have been or not."

"Who would I check with?" Ratsow asked. "I would like to see the items and also find out under what authority they took them."

"That I can tell you," Marty said.

"They took the artifacts under the Archaeological Resources Protection Act of 1979. Basically, it states that any material remains of past human life or activities that are of archaeological interest are protected, if it's a hundred years old."

"I thought that was for battlegrounds or designated areas," Ratsow said. "You were in the wilderness, weren't you?"

"Yah, but the law covers anything found on public or Indian land. If you want information about this or where the artifacts are, you will have to check with Bill Fox, the Special Agent with the Forest Service in Missoula, or the Forest Service Archaeologist, Milo McCloud, also from Missoula."

Ratsow studied his notes, then reached over and shut his tape recorder off. "Interesting story. Are you going to do anything more with this discovery?"

"If the Forest Service does an excavation and they invite me to go along, then I will, but I'm not going to try to find any more artifacts if I just have to give them up," Marty said.

"How about the gold?" Ratsow asked, smiling.

"What gold?" Marty asked, returning the reporter's smile. "If I did find gold, I'd just have to turn it over to the government, if it was related to the Magruder cases or any other human activity over a hundred years old."

"A man could never get rich doing that," Ratsow said, smiling, as he stood up. "Thanks for our time, Mr. Kincade. I'll get you a copy of the article over here this afternoon so you can read it before it goes to press." He shook Marty's hand, then left the office.

As he was descending the stairs, Ratsow wondered if this would be the last article he would write on the Lloyd Magruder case. *After all, legend has it there are thousands of dollars worth of gold buried out there somewhere by Magruder's murderers. Seems like it would be anticlimactic to end here,* he thought, *but what the hell do I know, I'm just a guy looking for a good story.*

17

Simon

Simon Wick couldn't believe what his eyes were reading. *This couldn't be the same Lloyd Magruder, but it must be.* He thought. The dates and places are the same ones mentioned in his great-great-grandfather's journal. Simon felt his heart beating more rapidly. The sudden rush of adrenaline caused him to nearly tear the treasure magazine in two as he flipped the pages to re-read the article. Frantically, he read the article's headline.

Detective Digs Up Evidence from Idaho's First Murder Case

Lewiston—A handful of nondescript bits of rusting metal may corroborate an outlaw's testimony and pinpoint the exact site of Lloyd Magruder's murder of 1863. A harness buckle, several square nails, a couple of .35 caliber lead balls, a metal corner that held a wooden box together and parts of a surveyor's tripod represent the only modern evidence of one of this region's first and possibly still most brutal crimes.

The artifacts were dug up by a Lewiston, Idaho, private detective last August. They appear to confirm the exact murder site of Lloyd Magruder and his packers, one hundred and twenty-nine years ago on October 11th, 1863.

The story went on to tell about Lloyd Magruder and his

enterprise, how the murder happened, and the subsequent trial and hanging of his murderers.

The article also gave an account of the private detectives and how they found the articles. But what caught Simon Wick's attention the most was the information about the gold. *Good God!* he said to himself. *That old man wasn't writing fantasy stories. He wasn't making things up. Crazy, yes, but that old boy was writing about real events.*

Simon read the article a third time. *Not a mistake,* he thought to himself. *It mention's Elk City, the store, the Bitterroot Mountains, Lewiston, Idaho; Virginia City, Bannack City. Damn!* He thought. *They used that old man's journal to write this article.*

Simon Wick sat in stunned silence. His great-great grandfather's writing was true then. There really was gold buried back in the Bitterroot Mountains of Idaho. Simon Wick didn't know what to think. He didn't even know what to do, but it slowly dawned on him that he just might be the only living human being to know that over a quarter million dollars in gold was, in fact, hidden out by some lonely mountain Indian trail deep in the wilderness.

Simon suddenly had a very strong urge to go home. Simon Wick wanted to read a journal. He wondered if his grandfather's journal would give a clue as to where the gold might be hidden.

Then his attention was drawn to the last paragraph in the article. It implied that the private detective might have discovered a clue about the hidden gold, but then the reporter more or less laughed that possibility off, as he admitted, it didn't hurt to dramatize an event a little. "After all, buried treasure sparked human interest, legend or not."

Simon folded the magazine and tucked it under his arm. *Why do that?* He thought to himself. *I've still got five hours to sit in this hole.* He grabbed the magazine and put it under the pillow on his bunk. *That is stupid,* he thought. *No one hides a magazine.* His common sense told him one thing, his anxiety and greed another.

Damn, he thought. *If that bitch Becky hadn't called the police, I wouldn't be here. I would be on a path to wealth, but I need to get the hell out of here because other people will read that damn article.*

Simon walked to his cell door and placed his hands on the bars. Moments later, he lowered his forehead against the cold steel. *Better cool down,* he thought to himself. *Don't do anything that will keep you in here any longer.*

Simon was serving the last of a ten-day sentence for battery. He wondered if Becky would have called the police if he would have really beat her up, instead of just cuff her around like he did. Maybe next time, that's what he would do, teach her a lesson.

"Damn women anyway," he said aloud, as his thoughts took him back two months ago.

Simon had been off work early that day, as his cab had broken down. The cab company dispatcher sent a tow truck and his cab was taken to a nearby garage, but the mechanic told him it would be at least until the next day before the cab would be back on the street. He hadn't even waited for the mechanic to tell him what the trouble was. In a rage, he simply walked two blocks up the street to "Lady Lucy's" and commenced to get drunk.

At seven o'clock that evening, Simon called the doorman to come get him. Simon called Billy Gilbert the doorman, because that's the only kind of work he had ever known him to have. *A natural born servant,* Simon had thought, when he first met Gilbert working at the Evandor Hotel, next to his cab stand.

Ever since that day, the two had been friends, at least Gilbert felt that way about the relationship. Simon merely tolerated the doorman because he quickly discovered the doorman was a great gofer. Simon liked the power he had over the doorman and Billy Gilbert liked Simon because he now had someone who at least recognized him and needed him. As a child growing up without parents, Billy Gilbert never had caring and recognition. As Simon's friend he had both, or so he thought.

When the doorman arrived at "Lady Lucy's," he found that Simon had been beat up. The bartender explained to the doorman that Simon had gotten fresh with one of the waitresses, and that her boyfriend was sitting at the bar when Simon grabbed her. He had only hit Simon one time, but that had been enough because Simon was ready to pass out anyway.

The doorman had taken Simon home that night. He saw Simon become belligerent when Becky tried to keep him in the house. He saw him hit Becky several times while he took his anger out on her. Although he didn't want to, he had called the cops on Simon that day. Becky had signed the complaint, but he had called the police. His only hope was that Simon was too drunk to remember that he had called, that he had prevented Simon from further assault on Becky.

The doorman was very thankful when Simon had plead guilty. Now he wouldn't have to testify against his best friend. He was very happy now because Becky had moved to Seattle last week. There wouldn't be any more fights between her and Simon. The doorman had liked Becky, but she did get in the way of his and Simon's friendship. Ever since Simon had met Becky three months ago, he had seen his friend less and less.

Now things would be back to normal, Becky was gone and Simon needed him again. That was the doorman's thinking, as he drove to the Multnomah County jail to pick up Simon Wick.

The five hours had seemed like five days to Simon, but at least his anger with Becky had subsided. At least now he could concentrate on the journal. The doorman had told him about Becky leaving. *Good riddance,* he thought. "I've got more important things to do than worry about her," he said aloud, while waiting for the doorman in front of the county jail. A black kid, who was walking by just then, said, "Know watcha mean, my man." His white teeth flashed with his wide smile.

Simon ignored the kid and started pacing back and forth on the sidewalk, his irritation and impatience starting to grow, as he looked at his watch.

He opened the treasure magazine and started to read the article again when the doorman pulled up to the curb. Simon opened the door and jumped in. "Take me home fast," he ordered. "We've got an adventure to go on and if things work out, we are going to be very rich men."

The doorman looked at Simon with a puzzled look. "I don't understand," he said.

"Drive," Simon repeated. "I'll explain on the way." As the doorman's 1984 Datsun pickup sped down the freeway, Simon told him about the article in the treasure magazine, omitting most of the truth. Instead, Simon told him that a private detective might have discovered some clues regarding hidden gold that once belonged to a relative of his. He went on to explain that his relative had been murdered and the gold was hidden by the murderers.

Simon continued to explain that he and the doorman were going to Idaho, to try to reclaim the gold that is rightfully his.

"But what about our jobs?" the doorman asked. "Harley, down at the cab company, said he was going to keep your job open until you got out of jail."

"Screw Harley and his cab company," Simon said.

"Screw your job at the Evandor, screw Becky, and screw this town. We are leaving and gonna get rich in doing it."

The doorman didn't like quitting his job, and he didn't really want to leave Portland to run off in some wilderness that he knew nothing about, but he didn't want to get Simon mad either. *Oh, what the hell,* he finally thought, *maybe we will get rich.*

When they arrived at Simon's apartment, Simon filled out a deposit slip and gave that and his paycheck from the cab company to the doorman. He then signed a blank personal check, then made out a list of camping and survival equipment.

"Deposit my paycheck," he ordered. "Then go and get everything on this list. When you get done, go home and pack. Then come back here and get me. I should be ready to go by then."

The doorman thought for a moment. He didn't like this. Everything was too sudden. "But what about all my stuff that I can't pack? What about my apartment and your apartment and your car?" he asked.

"Leave it all," Simon replied. "We'll buy everything new, later."

The doorman frowned. He didn't like this, but he drove off, obediently, to do as instructed.

After he was gone, Simon went to his bedroom. In a corner of the room was an old wooden chest, made sometime before World War II. It had been his mother's, and in it she had stored different items that had been in the family and passed down from generation to generation during the last hundred years. There were several diaries, a family Bible, numerous photographs of people from different eras, and other personal belongings.

Simon was looking for a small wooden chest. When he found it, he opened it slowly.

The journal inside was very old, and now, had a great deal of meaning to him. Not a sentimental meaning, he assured himself, but one of personal need. Something that most people would describe as greed. This feeling was only vaguely acknowledged by Simon, but despite his selfishness, a pang of awe and sentiment did stir him.

Simon opened the journal slowly. The first thing that caught his eye was a small key, attached to a pocket watch and chain. These were lying just under the front cover. A small, very old padlock lay beside the journal in the wooden box. Simon carefully placed the key, watch and chain in the small chest, wondering whose they were.

He carefully turned the journal's pages, scan-reading the beginning pages. Nothing significant at first, just dates that his grandfather had purchased mining claims and the legal descriptions. After several more pages, he stopped and turned back to the first page. He remembered that page had some information about his, *what would he be?* Simon thought as he read the page.

Journal II, Property of John Wick 1861
August 7th, 1861

I start this second journal, as I have run out of pages with the first. It seems that I'm running out of a lot of things lately. My mines are not doing well and other business ventures are failing. If things don't pick up soon, I may be forced to sell and move to the North. Rumor is, that other gold fields are being discovered in the Washington Territory. What they call Idaho.

August 8th, 1861

Janet says he won't go with me, as she just got a job working in a bakery. Who Cares, she can stay in the Damn bakery. I want to get rich.

Simon turned ahead to other pages. Then he saw the

name Lloyd Magruder. There, he started reading again. The first entry at the top of the page read:

June 2nd, 1862—Marysville
Janet asked for some personal things that women need. I told her such things were not worth spending money on. She started to cry, so I slapped her across the face. She really hollered then, so I kicked her in the ass.

Simon smiled to himself, "That old boy and I would get along," he said. "We have the same philosophy."

The next entry he read was July 3rd, 1862—Portland. It described his grandfather's original business deal with Magruder at the Vancouver Hotel.

It also described his grandfather's anger at Caroline Magruder for interfering in the deal. Simon, himself, started to get angry just reading the entry. He didn't blame his grandfather for hating the Magruders. *Damn*, he thought, *Magruder's old lady cost Grandpa 10 percent before he even started.*

Simon turned more pages, scanning. He read entries about meeting two men called Renton and Romain, but prior to that, there was a vague entry about Lloyd meeting three miners and an agreement of some kind between the men to haul gold from the mining camps. Simon couldn't tell if his grandfather was involved in this agreement or simply describing in his journal that he had heard about it.

The words were blotted and faint. Somehow over the years, a few drops of water had smeared much of the ink, destroying many words.

The next entry was also faded and many of the words were destroyed, probably with water, Simon thought, wondering how that could have happened.

Simon was unable to make out the date, but the entry was clear. Simon gasped at what his grandfather had written.

He had described a meeting with this Renton and Romain, and had gone into detail about how he wanted them to kill Magruder and his men. How he wanted them to bring the gold to a place called Granite Springs, after they made the murder look like an Indian attack. Then, he even wanted Renton and Romain to kill two others, who were to help with the murders. His grandfather wanted the other two men buried with the gold. *Good Lord,* Simon said to himself. *The man's vicious. I don't remember reading this six months ago when I first found this journal.* Intrigued, he continued on.

The next entry was dated August 18th, 1863. It described his grandfather's observation of Lloyd Magruder in a fight with a man by the name of O'Grady. Apparently it happened on a street in Elk City, probably Idaho Territory, Simon thought. What really startled Simon was the viciousness with which his grandfather tells how he would like to describe Magruder's death to his wife. With a shudder, Simon read that portion of the entry again.

> I wish I could tell his wife that I killed him and took all the gold he was saving for her. I wish I could tell her that she could have only 15% of her husband's lousy carcass, because the wolves got the rest and shit him out on some mountain ridge. The BITCH, BITCH, BITCH.

"One hateful son-of-a-bitch," Simon said softly, as he read on. The next entry was for the same day. It described how this O'Grady killed himself in a whore house and how disgusted his grandfather had become at the miners, whores, and Magruder.

The next entry, dated August 22, 1863, was even more shaking to Simon. He didn't remember reading this entry either. It described Lloyd Magruder leaving Elk City, with his mule train, but most important was the fact that his grandfather described going to Magruder's Ranch after he left town, then snooping in a desk, which was owned by someone named Morgan.

Apparently, this was someone who worked for Magruder, Simon thought. The entry went on and horribly described how his grandfather had returned to town and caught Morgan, inside the store, reading this very journal. It continued, with the description of how his grandfather had killed Morgan with a pick. *Maybe killed while reading this journal,* Simon thought and nearly let loose of the book, as though it were hot.

Simon read on, almost hypnotized by the writing. He hadn't been this intrigued six months ago when he first found and read the journal in the attic of his mother's house. Then again, he had only read a few of the entries at that time.

As he recalled, he had been drinking, so therefore was probably not as attentive as he could have been.

But, what the hell, he thought. His mother had died only a week before that and it was depressing going through her personals and selling off her property. Anyone else would have drank a few beers, too, he rationalized. Anyone, except Becky, that is. Simon's thoughts left the journal, as he remembered her helping him through that difficult time. Maybe he should be a little more understanding with her, he thought. No other woman had put up with him as long as she had. Maybe he should go to Seattle and get her, maybe even apologize.

No, that will have to wait, he thought, *at least until I get back from Idaho, with that gold.* Then he could take her a peace offering. Maybe even buy her that car, the Miata, she was saving for.

Simon turned the page, still thinking about Becky. He continued reading the entry. His grandfather described how he had taken Morgan's body out of town after dark, dug up the grave of the man O'Grady, then dumped Morgan's body on top of him.

His grandfather skipped a few days, but then entered into the journal an admission that he had started a rumor around that Morgan had quit for medical reasons, claiming to go to Portland to see a doctor about his leg.

The next significant entry was dated Friday, October 30, 1863. John Wick, in this entry, wrote about his frustrations that Renton and Romain had not shown up as scheduled. Nor had Magruder or any of his party. Wick wrote that he feared both groups may have "shot each other up."

He talked about a young miner who had delivered a letter to Sarah Maxwell, in Elk City, and that the letter had been from Magruder to his wife.

Wick expressed concern that the outlaw Romain might talk and if he did, "anything could happen." He concluded this entry by saying that he would give Romain a few more days and that if he didn't show up, he would leave Elk City.

Undoubtedly, his grandfather was getting worried about what had happened and also the whereabouts of the gold.

Simon, eager for a clue about the gold, turned more pages, scanning them. Most of the entries expressed anger or frustration about people whom his grandfather didn't like. Simon couldn't find any entry describing or documenting when his grandfather left Elk City, but he did find an interesting entry dated December 4th, 1864. The entry was made after his grandfather left Elk City and had arrived in San Francisco. It read:

December 4, 1864—San Francisco

It's been over a year now since I sent Romain and Renton out to deal with Magruder and get the gold. Like always, people have failed me. Shortly after I left Elk City, I learned that Magruder and party had, in fact, been killed. The newspapers indicated that one of Magruder's friends caught the murderers in Lewiston, after he found them in possession of Magruder's gun and horse. The stupid asses, serves them right as it's obvious they had doublecrossed me. That probably means they hid the gold somewhere other than Granite Springs, but where? The newspaper accounts said that $12,000.00 was found with the outlaws, but what happened to the gold Magruder was packing for the miners in Bannack City? They couldn't have taken it far, because, according to the latest articles in the papers, they shot all the mules near where they killed the men. If that is the case, then they would have had to bury it or hide it somewhere near the murder site. But if that is so, then why didn't someone find it? Or why didn't Renton and Romain or even those other two tell where it was at, in order to save their lives?

I will give credit to Renton and Romain. They didn't tell anyone I was behind all of this. I guess, maybe they figured one double cross in a lifetime is enough. They obviously didn't tell those other men that helped them either, what was there names? Lower and Page, I believe.

They hung Lower with Renton and Romain, so I'm sure they didn't say anything, because Page didn't mention my name when he was confessing to everything else.

It's been nine months now, since they hung Renton and Romain, so I feel I'm fairly safe. I've let my hair grow long and my beard as well, just to be on the safe side.

This coming spring, I'll go back and hunt for it. Apparently, for some reason, I'm the only one that seems to know about the gold from Bannack City. I know for sure, damn it, that Magruder was hauling miner's gold, because I heard him talking with those men myself about it. Romain also heard Magruder talking to his men about hauling the gold, just before they left Lewiston that summer.

I've never been beyond Granite Springs, so I would have no idea where their campsite is. Guess I'll just have to take

162

chances and go anyway. Maybe, I could get some clue about Magruder's letter from that Maxwell lady, if my name is clear around those parts.

Simon discovered that there were no more entries for over two years. The next entry was dated April 18th, 1867.

I can't let this gold consume me. I've tried to stop thinking about it and have forced myself to stop writing about it, or anything else for that matter. I've been back in the Bitterroots twice now, looking for it. I've found where they killed Magruder and his men, searched the area—NOTHING. I talked to a young man, by the name of Erand Michaels. He admitted that he brought a letter from Magruder to Sarah Maxwell in Elk City, but denied he made statements to anyone about Magruder carrying a lot of gold. He claimed that story was just rumor, but I talked with two different men, who said they were present at Toby's Saloon, in Elk City, when Erand bragged of such knowledge.
    I have asked Sarah Maxwell about the letter, she said she destroyed it, since Magruder was dead. Stated she didn't want to upset his wife any further, by giving it to her.

The next entry was dated five months later.

September 20, 1867—San Francisco
    I have been sick lately. I hate this warehouse job, I hate life. My only pleasure is repaying Janet for stealing my money. Fate has been good by delivering her into my hands. As soon as she gives me my son, I will have even more pleasure. Janet will learn not to double-cross me. Soon, she will do with many others, what she does with me now.

Simon read on, but then stopped. What his grandfather was describing now were unspeakable sexual acts that wouldn't be tolerated in any society. He could hardly believe his grandfather had become so perverted, so cruel. Yet in reading the journal, he was faintly aware that he got a small touch of satisfaction on behalf of his grandfather.

Near the end of the entry, his grandfather wrote something positive about another human being. His grandfather had apparently read a newspaper account regarding the hanging of Romain, Renton, and Lower in Lewiston. He wrote:

Regarding that double-crossing scoundrel, Romain. I can't help but respect and admire him. He didn't turn me in and his last words, before the noose stretched him, were excellent. "I request to be buried face down, so the people of Lewiston can kiss my butt forever." What defiant courage the man had.

Simon observed this was the last sentence of his grandfather's journal.

Simon sat on his bed, staring at the remaining blank pages. He was confused with conflicting emotions, as he reflected on his grandfather's writings. Slowly, the remaining empty pages began to turn as the journal lay on his lap. Simon's attention returned to the now rapidly closing pages. He automatically reached up and placed his hand on the journal. He stopped the pages near the very end. He realized that he was looking at yet another entry in the journal, but this entry was made by someone else. The handwriting was noticeably different. "Probably a woman's hand writing," Simon speculated. The entry was dated October 11th, 1867.

I make this last entry in the journal of John Wick. I say last, because it certainly will be, for I have murdered John Wick. I now feel tremendous relief and, at least for the present, I do not feel any guilt. I gave John Wick a full bottle of Laudanum, besides applying a pillow over his face for a considerable length of time. I take no particular pleasure in what I have done. I simply did what I had to do, kill or be killed. If I am wrong, then God have mercy on my soul.

One can only partially understand the demonic soul of this evil man, by reading the writings of this journal. Living with him, in person, was not unlike the worst nightmare one could imagine. The writings and admissions of John Wick describe a horrible crime, in the killing of Mr. Magruder and party. If his murderers had not been brought to justice, then I would have turned this journal in to the proper authorities. Since they have been dealt with, and I have dealt with Mr. Wick, I see no need in exposing the family name to ridicule and shame.

I shall bear John Wick's son and with the grace of God, he shall be raised a good, kind and decent man. I shall name him Simon and pray I never have to show him this journal. If he accepts Buck Welch as his father, then perhaps I will not have to. May God have mercy and give us both guidance. In his name, I pray.

Janet Wick

Simon closed the journal and clutched it to his chest. He lay back on his bed. His mind was in a whirl. *My father's name was Simon and so was Grandpa's. Obviously, Great-grandfather was also called Simon, but his father was John. John Wick.* Simon lay on his bed for a long time. His gaze centered on a small dark spot on the ceiling.

18

Bitterroot Gold

At 9:00 A.M., Tom Haugstad's phone rang. He didn't want to answer it. Deep inside his head, the sleeping man yelled curses at the telephone. It continued to ring. He put his pillow over his head, but that didn't help. Rude, belligerent, and persistent, the ringing continued.

Angrily, Tom reached out and grabbed the phone. Nearly dropping it, he slapped it down on the pillow vacated by his wife three hours ago. Picking up the receiver, he shouted. "This better not be a damn salesman."

There was a pause, then the familiar laugh of Marty Kincade broke through the fuzzies. "Woke you up, did I?"

Tom, recognizing Kincade's voice, finally muttered, "Oh, hi, chief, what's doin'?"

Kincade continued, "How soon can you get ready to go into the back country, say for a week, maybe two?"

Haugstad tried to absorb this information, but his mind was still a little slow. "Back country? We got a case in the back country?"

"No," the voice answered back. "Gold, my man. We are going after gold. Bitterroot gold, to be exact."

Tom Haugstad thought a moment, then it came to him. "We going after the gold Magruder was packin'?" he finally asked.

"That's right," Kincade said. "I want to leave just as soon as you can get your gear ready. I've already got all of my stuff in the Blazer. The only thing that I've got left to do is pick up another metal detector and I'll do that while you are packing."

"Thought we had a missing person case to work on today," Haugstad grumbled.

"Solved it last night. Now quit stalling," Kincade said. "We have a long way to go. We are going to Dixie."

"Dixie!" Haugstad said.

"Yah, Dixie. I found a guy there by the name of Howard Williams. He's ninety-four years old and he's the son of Lucy Maxwell Williams."

"Who in hell is Lucy Maxwell Williams?" Tom asked, still not convinced this information justified the disturbance of his sleep.

"Lucy Maxwell Williams is the daughter of Sarah Maxwell. Sarah is the woman who received Lloyd Magruder's letter before he was killed. Lucy showed this same letter to Grandpa over forty years ago. Remember, I've told you all about it."

Slowly the significance of this information dawned on Haugstad. "You mean this old man, Williams, has the letter?" Tom asked.

"Don't know," Marty replied. "I've only talked to him on the phone, but he says that he's got a lot of things of his mother's. Bibles, journals, photos of family and papers he's never really gone through. Says he's never seen a letter of Lloyd Magruder's that was held by his mother, but he also said it could be there because he's never gone through a lot of her personal affects. He said that he was in Europe during the war when she died and was never familiar with the Magruder case or other local history."

"Well, why'n hell is he living in Dixie then? That's thirty miles more remote than Elk City, isn't it?"

167

"Yah, it is," Marty said. "Mr. Williams claims Lucy had moved to Dixie from Elk City just before she died and when he returned to the states in 1946, he continued to live on her place."

"Seems like a long shot to me, boss," Tom said in a last feeble protest.

"Probably is," Marty agreed. "But it's better than anything else that's come along in the last hundred years. I'll pick you up in an hour. Tell your wife that you are going to try and make her a rich woman. She'll let you go," Marty said, as he hung up the phone.

Yah, right, Tom thought. *She already thinks you're a jerk for keeping me gone all last week.* He looked at the phone a few moments, then hung up the receiver.

An hour later, Marty Kincade drove into his driveway. The Blazer was loaded down with camping gear and Tom could see him grinning from ear to ear. *Glad he's happy,* he thought, as Marty got out of the Blazer.

"You ready? Come on. Let's go. I don't want that old guy to die before we get there."

"We'll probably die before that old fart does," Tom countered.

"Maybe," Marty said, "but I don't want to give him any more opportunity than I have to."

Tom grinned. "Well, I'm ready. Help me load my gear," he said, as he raised his garage door. "By the way, I'm taking my 9mm. How about you?"

"Taking my .45," Marty replied. "I'm also going to take this new Rugar .22 I bought last week." Marty reached inside the Blazer and grabbed the rifle. "Thought we could bang a few ground squirrels on the way in." He handed the gun to Tom.

"Model 1020, huh?" Tom said, as he examined the rifle. "What's the clip hold?"

"The clip in it holds ten, but I've got a banana clip that holds thirty."

"No squirrel's gonna get away from you," Tom snorted, as he handed the carbine back to Marty.

In three minutes, they had Tom's gear loaded and in fifteen, they were headed out of town on Highway 95, southbound for Dixie.

They traveled in silence for nearly an hour, but finally Tom's curiosity overcame his irritation.

"Okay, I give up," he spouted. "You find a long-lost treasure map or something? I mean, there must be some reason you're dragging me back to Magruder Ridge. It can't be artifacts, because the Forest Service made it clear we can't take any more from the murder site, so it must be the letter Magruder sent to his wife just before he was killed. You believe her son, this Howard Williams, has the letter, don't you? You also know this letter can't be confiscated by the Forest Service because it is and has been in the possession of this Williams guy an his ancestors. You want this letter because it's a major historical find, that's been lying around under everyone's nose for a hundred and thirty years. We aren't going to Magruder Ridge again, are we? We're just going to this old guy, Williams's place, find this letter, then con him out of it. Right? How am I doin'?" Tom asked.

Marty glanced at him and smiled. "You have some of it right, but there's more," Marty said.

Tom looked at him for several moments, then his smug smile slowly left his face. "We are going back to Magruder Ridge, aren't we? You really believe this lost gold story, don't you?" he asked, with genuine exasperation.

Marty smiled again, but the mask of guilt that covered his face was unmistakable.

"What the hell is it?" Tom asked. "What the hell do you know that you are not telling me?"

169

Marty was quiet for nearly a minute. He drew in a deep breath, then spoke. "I think I've already seen the gold. I think we already found it."

"What!" Tom said, almost yelling. "What the hell are you talking about, Marty?"

Again Marty took in a deep breath. "Last year, when we were at the murder site, do you remember right after we found the artifacts? You went down the side of the ridge—what, maybe a hundred yards. You were sweeping the hill below the campsite, as we figured from Page's testimony that we might find debris three that the bandits had thrown away in an attempt to hide evidence."

"Yah, I remember," Tom said. "I probably worked the hill-side for nearly an hour, but there was nothing there. Not even a bleep on the detector."

Marty started to speak, paused, then continued. "While you were down over the hill, I continued to probe the camp-site. In the process of doing that, my shovel broke through the earth about a foot down. I used my pen light and looked into the hold that I'd made. At first, I couldn't believe my eyes. I was looking into a hole or some kind of cave. Probably just a natural space or hole, because there were large granite rocks all around this space. It looked to me like the entire ridge was a huge pile of rock and this was just a space between all the rocks."

"Probably just that," Tom said. "That whole country is granite rock."

Marty signed and gave Tom a patient grin. "Humor me," Marty said, "and I'll finish the story."

"By all means," Tom replied, as he made a "before me" gesture with his arm and hand.

"Anyway," Marty continued, "while I was looking down into the hole, I spotted what looked like wooden boxes. They appeared to be rotten and falling apart, but you couldn't mistake them as boxes. In fact, it looked like some of them had writing on the sides. I couldn't make the words out though, because of the deterioration. A couple of boxes had fallen apart. I could see rocks in them and it looked like gold ore. I'm sure as hell no miner, but I tell you, I believe I was looking at thousands of dollars in gold."

Tom stared at Marty. He started to speak, but stopped. Finally, he asked, "Why didn't you say something when you saw this?"

Marty blushed, embarrassed by his lack of honesty with his friend.

"I started to, wanted to, but then I started thinking. If what I saw is gold, Magruder's gold, then we wouldn't have been able to get it out last year. As you remember, we were there in late September. By mid-October that country is snowed in. I guess what it boils down to, is security. If you made a slip to your wife or kids and they made a slip to someone else, well, you can figure it out. I guess I thought I would wait a year and tell you on our way back in here, thus eliminating a risk, or so I thought. As you know, I almost blew it by telling too many people about the artifacts. The next thing you know, the press is knocking on our door, then the Forest Service. I felt I had to talk to the press about the artifacts or some nosy reporter might just decide to make his own investigation at the Magruder site."

"Well, now what?" Tom asked. "We can't take the gold because it's part of man's activity and that falls under the Archaeological Resources Protection Act of 1979."

"Yah, I know, but I figure we can take part of it, then turn the rest in, along with the letter if we want to do that. I thought I'd talk it over with you and see what you wanted to do."

Tom looked at Marty. "Well, that's nice, that you're going to talk things over with me. That I appreciate."

Marty grinned, as a slight blush crossed his face.

"Hell, yes. I want to keep some of the gold. Hell, let's keep it all and give the government the rotten boxes for their artifacts. As far as the letter goes, well, we don't even know if it exists, or do we? Is there something else you haven't told me?" Tom asked.

Marty winced. "Yah, but it's not the letter and it's no big deal. We are just going to pick up a couple of horses and trailer from my uncle. He has a ranch just this side of Grangeville. In fact," Marty said, "the turnoff to his place is only a quarter mile up the road."

Several moments later, Marty signaled for a left turn. The Blazer turned from the highway at some grain elevators surrounded by five houses. Marty referred to it as the "Town of Fenn," as they passed the only roadside store, which Tom suspected was the oldest country market in the world.

"Well, what other surprises do you have for me? Tom asked. "What about this letter of Magruder's you keep talking about? Do you have it tucked away some place?"

"No, no," Marty replied. "It's just that I'm sure it exists. Grandpa claims he read it and that was about a year before Lucy died. Just before she died, she moved to Dixie. After her death, her son Howard Williams moved into her place and has been there ever since. When I talked with him on the phone the other day, he told me that he has no other close relatives and that he has never thrown anything of his mother's out. So, I would say there is a better than average chance the letter is still in Lucy's personals. Probably hasn't been read since Grandpa read it in the early 40's."

"Why did this Lucy let your grandpa read it?" Tom asked.

"Well, I guess Grandpa used to help her with a gold mine she was running. He said she was ill and couldn't work much, so he helped her out. I guess one day they were talking about gold and the subject of Magruder came up. According to Grandpa, Lucy never told anybody about the letter or let anyone else read it. Grandpa says the people in Elk City minded their own affairs and didn't pry into anyone else's. I suppose that's why the letter was never discovered. Why hell, that letter was over eighty years old when Grandpa read it."

Tom thought about that for a while, then asked, "I understand the historical importance of the letter, but I don't see how it's going to help us all that much, if you already know where the gold is."

"I've got more interest in this than just gold. If there is valuable information in that letter, then I would like to be the one who says what should happen to it."

"What would you do with it?" Tom asked.

"I'd give it to the Luna House Museum, in Lewiston. That's where Lloyd sent it. Of course it was a hotel then, but I'm sure Lloyd wouldn't object. After all, he was a citizen of Lewiston. Besides, it may give us some information about the gold and the bandits. As I recall, Grandpa said the letter mentioned Lloyd's fear of being attacked. I guess I would like to find out as much as I can about the murders and all the facts surrounding them."

Tom thought for several minutes and stared out the window of the Blazer as they passed grain and barley fields. Finally, he asked, "We takin' the horses to pack the gold out?"

"Yep," Marty replied.

"What happens if we get to Dixie and find that Mr. Williams got curious, found the letter, and turned it over to the sheriff or something?"

"Not much chance of that," Marty said. "Mr. Williams doesn't like the sheriff. Seems one of the deputies gave him a ticket last month for driving his jeep without license plates or a driver's license. Williams told me he couldn't get a driver's license because his eyes were so bad that he couldn't read to take the driver's test. One of the first questions he asked me was I a deputy or with the government in any way. When I assured him that I was a private investigator, he agreed to talk with me."

Tom smiled in thought. "You know, chief, some people would have a hard time staying sober around you."

Marty laughed, then turned the Blazer onto the dirt lane leading to his uncle's ranch.

"Is your uncle going with us?" Tom asked.

"Naw. He left on vacation yesterday. Said he would have the horses corralled and all's we will have to do is hook onto the trailer and go. He's got the saddles, packsacks, and hay already loaded in the trailer. We'll be out of here in twenty minutes, if the horses load okay."

Marty stopped in Grangeville long enough to purchase some white gas for the Coleman stove and a box of .45 caliber ammo. In fifteen minutes, they were out of town, descending the Mount Idaho Grade to the south fork of the Clearwater River, where the highway would parallel the river to Elk City. After leaving Elk City, they would travel another twenty-five miles over a narrow, winding mountain road to reach Dixie.

The trip was slow, at thirty-five miles an hour, but it gave Tom a chance to re-enjoy the scenery, which he had appreciated so much the year before. *This country is so beautiful and rugged, it's almost amazing,* he thought, as he realized they were climbing and the trees were different. The lower river country consisted of white fir and cedar. They were now into the forest of small jack pine, dotted with openings of lush mountain meadows. *An elk hunter's paradise,* Tom thought. They had been traveling for over an hour, but it seemed like minutes to Tom.

The mountain community of Dixie had fifteen year-round residents, but the population swelled to a hundred during the summer and fall. Part-time miners and retired couples made up the bulk of the population.

The commercial area included a bar, restaurant, motel, post office, and grocery store. One could also get gasoline from the 1933 hand pump, still in operation, in front of the grocery store. Tom marveled at the pump. "I've only seen one like this in pictures."

"Could you top us off, Tom?" Marty asked, as he stopped the Blazer beside the pump.

"The scale on the glass says it only holds ten gallons."

"Yah, you have to work that handle on the side of the pump to put more gas into it. We probably need twenty gallons, so you can play with it awhile. I'll ask whoever's in the restaurant where Mr. Williams lives."

Tom nodded as he left the Blazer and stood staring at the antique gas pump.

Marty went inside and noticed that a heavy-set woman was both cook and waitress. There was only one customer and the woman had just served him his breakfast. She glanced at Marty with a smile and said, "We're not open today, but if you're hungry, guess I could feed you."

Marty glanced at the man eating, which the woman noticed.

"That's just my husband. He's always eating."

Marty surmised that she also did her share of eating.

"Well, if it's no trouble, ma'am," Marty said, "we could use some bacon and eggs. We left early this morning and didn't eat. We're getting gas, so my friend will come over soon as he finishes, then pays for it."

"Tell him to come over here and pay for it," the woman said. "We own the store and the pump, too." Marty stuck his head back out the restaurant door and told Tom to come over when he was finished.

The woman had their breakfast ready in about ten minutes and was just setting the steaming food on the table when Tom entered. "Smells good, looks good," Tom said, as he sat at the table with Marty.

"It will taste good, too," Marty said. "Seems like everything tastes better in the mountains."

The woman came out of the kitchen to fill their coffee cups, when Marty asked her where Howard Williams lived. "Down about a hundred fifty yards on your left," she replied. "Log cabin right as you leave town. Say, are you boys lookin' for the Magruder gold, too?" she asked.

Marty burnt his lip on the coffee as he was just taking a drink. Tom dropped a fork full of scrambled eggs on the table.

Marty finally asked, "Who was looking for the Magruder gold?"

"Couple fellers came in here last night and stayed at our motel. They just left a couple hours ago. Said they was writers and a goin' to do a story about Magruder. They said they wanted to talk with Mr. Williams."

"How—why did they want to talk to Mr. Williams?" Marty blurted, almost rudely.

The woman looked at Marty a little funny, then said, "They just asked if anyone around these parts knew anything about the murders. I told them to talk with Howard. He's the oldest in these parts and if anybody knew anything, he would. Seems Howard told me one time, that his grandmother, Sarah Maxwell, knew and was friends with Magruder. But you'd have to ask him to be sure, though."

Marty and Tom quickly finished their breakfast, and after paying for it and the gas, hurried down the road to William's cabin.

Marty knocked at the door, which was opened almost immediately by Howard Williams.

"You the detective?" he asked before Marty could introduce himself.

"Yah—yes, sir. I am, and you must be Mr. Williams."

"I am, son. Come on in. Been expecting you."

Before Williams could say anything else, Marty asked about the other men who had been inquiring about the Magruder case.

"Yep. One of them said he was a great-great-grandson of John Wick, who was Magruder's partner in the store at Elk City. Said he was trying to find out about his family heritage, but I know better'n that. He was a-lookin' for gold. Asked a lot of questions about gold and if I knew anything about hidden gold in the area. He's a real tenderfoot, that one is and I don't like him one bit," Williams said. "He reminds me of a damn weasel. Probably just as crooked as his kin, John Wick."

"How do you know about a John Wick, Mr. Williams?" Marty asked.

"Folks around Elk City talked about him some. They tell me my mother and grandmother used to talk about him being a crook and that they suspected him of stealing money from Magruder's store after he was killed. Just stories, mind you, but I sure didn't like this Simon feller, who claims to be his kin. The other guy didn't say word one, so can't say much about him."

"Excuse me, Mr. Williams, but I didn't introduce myself or my friend. I'm Marty Kincade and this is Tom Haugstad. I'm the one who talked with you on the phone."

"Yes, I know," Howard replied. "I can't see very good, but I can still hear, even though I do use hearing aids." Williams smiled then. "I suppose your next question is: did I talk to them about the letter and the answer is no. They didn't even ask about it, probably don't even know about it. How did you say you knew about it, Mr. Kincade?"

"My grandfather, sir. My grandfather read it one time while visiting your mother, Lucy. I believe Grandpa worked for her."

"I believe that's a fact," Williams replied. "Mother often mentioned your grandfather to me in her letters while I was serving in Europe. She thought a lot of him. I suppose I owe your grandfather a lot, since he kinda took my place helping Mother and all. I never did meet your grandfather, but I did see him one time, at Mother's funeral. He was just leaving the cemetery and someone pointed him out to me."

"How old would your grandfather be if he was still alive? I assume he has passed away."

"Yes, sir," Marty said. "He passed away in 1980. He would have been a hundred years old this last June."

"Six years older than me, huh," Howard stated as he turned and walked to his kitchen table. He picked up a letter that was very old and yellowed. Marty knew immediately that it must be Magruder's letter.

Howard talked as he handed the letter to Marty. "Found this in Mother's Bible, I think it's what you are looking for. I can't see very well, but with my magnifying glass, I think I make out the name of Magruder. I got curious after your phone call, so I started going through her things."

Marty took the letter and opened it very carefully. Immediately, he saw that it was addressed to Caroline Magruder of Lewiston, Idaho Territory. It read:

My Dearest Caroline,
Although I've been gone but a short time, it truly seems like years.

Marty read soberly for the next few minutes, stopping only long enough to sort out words and letters that had faded over the years.

When he was finished, Tom Haugstad noticed a small tear form in Marty's eyes. Only then did Tom realize that this case was more than just an adventure for Marty Kincade.

"Would you mind reading it aloud, son? If it's been in my family this many years, I would at least like to know what we were protecting," Howard said.

Marty looked at him and nodded. He started reading where he left off reading aloud the first time.

I have been away from you before, have missed you terribly before, but this time seems so different. I don't know why, maybe it's these mountains. They are so vast, so majestic, so . . . so very lonely. I suppose that's it. I'm traveling in an atmosphere that is tremendous in its loneliness. Even though there is life all around us, it seems like life is empty here. I feel kind of like I did when I was a boy back in Maryland. Kind of like the night before I left my home and family.

It's kind of an empty feeling. I suppose if I keep taking pity on myself, I will manage to get even lonelier. I will have to admit, my feelings are brought on by my own actions.

I keep pulling the beautiful watch you gave me and looking at your picture. Many a time, I looked at your picture, then turned in my saddle and looked at the beautiful blue mountains that we've crossed.

Often, I wanted to turn my horse around and ride back to you. Often, a tear has started in my eye, but I managed to suppress it before Charles or Bill could see.

I suppose, my darling, that I'm rambling on and probably don't make a lot of sense. I will ask that you forgive me and consider that it's just the ramblings of a lovesick fool.

It just seems that I've never had these kind of emotions or feelings before. Maybe it's just that I regret not having told you of my love more often.

I suppose that I had better write what I need to, as the fellow I'm giving this letter to will be leaving shortly.

A young man by the name of Erand, shall deliver this letter to the Luna House around the 15th of October. I have requested him to have Hill or Margaret deliver this to you post haste. I shall arrive in Lewiston two weeks later. Today is the 5th of October and we are in Bannack, but will be leaving here today for Elk City.

I bring with me, my dear, our fortune. I am pleased to report that our supplies brought over $20,000.00 in gold. I shall make another three thousand, as I'm bringing with me a large shipment of gold ore for some very fortunate friends of Lester Morgan. I will explain the details when I next see you.

I will say that I'm a bit uneasy in carrying all of this gold, as in the past, there has been a great deal of shooting and killing. I do believe, however, that most of the desperadoes have either been hung or run from the country. The ringleader of these desperate men was none other than their sheriff in Virginia City, Henry Plummer.

They hung him and several others shortly before we arrived in Virginia City. I wonder, my dear, if you remember this loathsome scoundrel. Last year, he stayed overnight at the Luna House. He introduced himself to us and Hill and Margaret when he registered.

Even though the toughs of the area have been dealt with, I shall maintain a strong vigilance during the night. You see, the mine owners have reinforced me with two of their men, who are very handy with gun. They had been Texas Rangers before coming to the territory. I have also hired two other men, who are armed and both have experience with mules. God knows, I need the help, as you see, I purchased more mules and our pack string now numbers one hundred twenty mules. We lost three mules on the way in, but I shall go into the explanation about that when I see you.

The next thing I want to mention, however briefly, is this. On my trip in here, I have requested from Elk City, that my name be put in for nomination at the Democratic Convention for representative from Idaho Territory to the Congress in Washington D.C. Over fifty citizens from Nez Perce County have signed my letter.

I have great hopes that I shall be successful. If I am, many of our lost hopes can be recovered and we can return to our home, proving to your family and mine, that our endeavors were indeed worthwhile. I am sorry for not informing you of my plans before, but I could not stand to see you go through another of my failures. This time, things are different, for we are now financially successful. In a short month, I shall be with you again, my dear, and God willing, I will never leave you again.

Give my best to Hill and Margaret and my love to John Carter and Eliza Lloyd.

Forever yours and Faithful Husband,

Lloyd

After Marty finished the letter, all three men sat without speaking. Each man was lost within his own thoughts and considering his own emotions.

Finally, Howard spoke softly. "The poor man nearly had the world by the tail. It's too bad that his letter didn't get to Lewiston. At least his wife would have had some consolation, and maybe, Hill Beachy and the others could have made the bandits tell where they hid all that gold. I suppose if my Grandmother Sarah had been able to read, it would have gotten to Lewiston."

Tom and Marty looked at the old man. "You're probably right," Marty said, at last. "She probably wanted to protect Lloyd's privacy, so she hung on to it, not knowing what to do. People in those days were generally more loyal to each other than they are now."

"I wonder how Sarah got the letter from this Erand fellow?" Tom asked.

"I don't know," Howard said. "My grandmother died before I was born and Mother never mentioned anything about this letter or Lloyd Magruder, but of course, I left home at thirteen, so I missed out on a lot of family history. In fact, I only saw my mother a few times as an adult."

"Could I have this letter, Mr. Williams?" Marty asked. "I would like to see that it finally gets to the Luna House."

Howard looked at Marty. "By all means, that's what I gave it to you for. I think it's probably been in my family long enough."

Marty and Tom smiled at each other. "We probably had better get going, Mr. Williams. I suspect there is still more to this story than what's been discovered," Marty said. "It's strange that a down line relative of John Wick's should happen on the scene at this point and time."

"Maybe not so strange," Howard said. "This Simon feller told me that he had become interested in his grandfather's heritage after reading an article in a treasure magazine the other day."

Marty looked at Tom. Both had read the same article. "It's a wonder every treasure hunter within five hundred miles isn't up here," Tom said.

"Mr. Williams, I can't thank you enough. This really means a lot to me, but I suppose we had better get going. We have a long way to go and, maybe, some interference with what I want to do," Marty said.

"Wish I could go with you," Howard said. "It sounds like a hell of an adventure."

"It is, sir, it is," Marty said, as he opened the cabin door to leave.

Marty and Tom walked out and just as Marty was closing the door, Howard said, "You know where the gold's at, don't you, Boy?"

Marty hesitated and for a split second he saw his grandfather standing where Howard had been. Marty nearly said, "Yah, Grandpa, we finally found it," but instead, he simply said, "Yes sir, I think so." He shut the old man's door and got into the Blazer beside Tom.

They drove the next fifteen miles back to the Red River Ranger Station without saying anything.

Tom was the first to break their silence. "Several questions come to my mind, chief," he said. Marty looked at him as he continued. "What are we going to do if this Simon guy is hanging around the area and decides he wants to tag along? Or better yet, what happens if he somehow knows where the gold is hidden himself and decides he doesn't want to part with it. Maybe he figures that he's got some kinda claim to it."

Marty considered a moment, then said, "I don't see how it's possible he could know about the extra gold Magruder was packing, but if he did and got to it first, I guess I'd just have to run up to the Magruder Ranger Station and radio Bill Fox in Missoula. I'd tell him that someone was stealing artifacts from the Magruder murder site. Fact of the matter is, I'm going to turn at least half of the gold over to Bill anyway. You and I can split the other half."

"Won't your Forest Service friend have something to say about that?" Tom asked.

"Probably, if he knew about it. I intend to get our share out of there before I tell the Forest Service about it."

Tom thought in silence for several moments, and then Marty continued.

"Grandpa looked for this gold for over forty years, off and on. I've looked for it nearly thirty years myself. Maybe I'm justifying my actions, but I feel if I found it, I keep it. It wouldn't help history or do anything to damage the Forest Service's archaeological investigation of the murder site, so I'm going to keep part of it. I can use a few thousand for my efforts, and I'm sure you can."

Tom grinned. "You've got that right. I just hope we can get our share before anyone finds out we have found it. If, in fact, we have. Those boxes you saw might hold something besides gold."

"I saw the gold, too," Marty reminded him. "I've seen the Bitterroot Gold."

19

Magruder Ridge

Pilot Creek was the halfway point to Magruder Crossing, over the very rough Darby Montana road, that wound, twisted, and climbed its way through the rugged Bitterroot Mountains.

Although Pilot Creek had an area big enough for six or seven camps, Marty had decided that he would stop only long enough to exercise and water the horses. It meant getting to the Magruder Crossing camp ground and setting up camp after dark, but he didn't like leaving saddle horses in a trailer that many hours without a break. On this road, the horses had to continually brace themselves and fight for footing in order to stay on their feet.

"This the Pilot Creek Camp?" Tom asked, as Marty slowed the Blazer to a stop at the first big campsite nearest the road.

"Yep," Marty answered. "A lot of people traveling through to Montana camp here, because it's the only real campsite with water. Besides that, the stream is loaded with ten-inch brookies."

"That's for me," Tom said. "I brought my pole."

"Not now, pard," Marty said, "I want to push on to Magruder Crossing, get what we can in the morning, and be on our way out of here by tomorrow evening. For some reason, I believe we only have so much time."

"Maybe, because too many people think they know about the gold," Tom said.

Marty nodded. "If you will make us a sandwich, I'll unload and water the horses, maybe walk them down the road a little ways."

"Okay, chief," Tom said, as he examined their cooler for sandwich makings.

At the next campsite, a few yards away, an elderly couple watched them, with mild curiosity, from their camper. Marty smiled and waved to them as he walked the horses past their camper to the creek. In the campsite just beyond the elderly couple, there was only one other camp. Two men had a small tent pitched beside their Datsun pickup. One man was underneath the vehicle, working on the muffler system, while the other was leaning over the hood of the Datsun, studying a Forest Service map. Marty observed that their license plate was an Oregon license.

Billy Gilbert swore and worked his way out from under the pickup. "I can't fix this without tools, Simon," he complained.

"Go ask those guys who just pulled in," Simon said, in an uninterested tone. "Maybe they have some tools." Billy Gilbert looked at Simon. He was beginning not to think of Simon as a friend. He was tired of being used, tired of being ordered around, tired of being treated like a nobody. At first, Simon had been nice to him, but as time went along, he had changed. He was mean to Becky first, then he started being mean to him. Now, he was being mean to everyone. He was even mean to the old people camped next to them.

What was that he had said to them as the old people watched them drive into the campground, with his tailpipe torn loose from the muffler. "Take a picture. It will last longer." What kind of a thing is that to say to old people?

Billy liked old people. They were good to him and tipped

him well as the doorman at the Evandor in Portland. Billy wished he would have stayed in Portland. He liked his job and now he was going to lose it, because Simon made him leave.

Billy thought Simon was stupid to come looking for buried treasure in the mountains. There was no way they could find gold in this big of a country, with this many trees. Even Simon said he didn't know exactly where to look. Simon even said that book of his grandfather's didn't tell where the gold is, so how would they ever find it?

Billy was muttering to himself as he walked up to Tom Haugstad, who was just making a second sandwich. "Hello. My name is Billy Gilbert. I've got a broken muffler. Do you have any tools so I can fix it?"

Tom was a little surprised at the way the man made his request and wondered if he wasn't a little retarded. Billy waited for Tom's answer, with an innocent, simple look on his face. Tom decided the man might not be completely retarded, but he was certainly "slow."

"Could I borrow your wrenches?" Billy asked a second time.

Tom shrugged his shoulders. "Sure, help yourself," he said, as he retrieved Marty's tool box from the Blazer and handed it to Billy. "Where you guys headed?" Tom asked. "Toward Montana or coming from Montana?"

"We are going to find Simon's grandfather's gold. Simon thinks some bad men buried it a long time ago and we're going to find it, but I don't think we can. I'm afraid to tell Simon though, 'cause he gets mad at me."

Tom was stunned at Billy's revelation. He decided that these must be the two men who had questioned Howard Williams and the woman at the Dixie restaurant.

"Where do you think the gold is?" Tom asked Billy.

"Don't know," he replied. "Simon says maybe where the

186

people were killed. He says he knows that place from what his grandfather wrote in the book."

"What book is that?" Tom asked.

"The book Simon has," Billy replied. "Thanks for the tool box. I'll bring it back," Billy said, as he walked back to his pickup.

Tom watched Billy Gilbert return to his pickup and climb under it. The man studying the map paid no attention to his partner's return.

Damn, where is Marty? Tom thought. *He needs to know this.*

The man on the Datsun's hood put the map away and knelt down beside Gilbert, who was working under the pickup. After a while, he glanced over at Tom.

The name on the tag riveted to the tool box rang a bell for Simon. "Property of Marty Kincade." *Where in hell have I heard that name before?* Simon looked over at the man eating a sandwich beside the horse trailer. Finally, he shrugged. Neither of them looked familiar.

"How much longer, doorman?" Simon asked.

"I have to loosen the clamp, then put the pipe back on the muffler, then tighten it again, then I'm done."

"Well, hurry up. I'm getting hungry and I want you to start dinner."

Billy Gilbert did something then that surprised himself more than it did Simon. He talked back to Simon. Except to prevent further assault on Becky, the doorman had never defied Simon. Until now, that is. Billy slid out from under the Datsun and faced Simon. "Fix dinner yourself, Simon. I'm busy."

Simon Wick was so astonished that he didn't say anything to the doorman. After a while, he quit staring at the doorman and did start fixing dinner.

A few minutes later, Tom walked over to get the tool box.

187

He wanted to look at Simon and size him up. Simon's dirty jeans, dingy shirt, missing front tooth, and out of style Princeton haircut told Tom what he wanted to know. *Looks like a small-time thief,* Tom thought. *Probably a shoplifter or some bum who spends most of his time on workmen's compensation, maybe both,* he concluded.

When Marty returned with the horses, Tom filled him in on the conversation with Billy Gilbert and his own estimation of Simon Wick.

"I don't think they are much to worry about," Tom said. "They sure aren't prepared for this country, especially if it snows. I don't think they even have pack sacks to carry any gold, if they did find it."

"Damn slugs," Marty said. "They did get this far, though, so we'd better keep a lookout for them just the same."

"They are both wearing tennis shoes, so they won't have an easy go getting up Magruder Ridge, if that's where they intend to go," Tom said.

"They probably won't find the ridge, even though it's marked on the Forest Service map," Marty said. "Anyway, let's get going. We've still got two and a half hours of travel time before we make camp at the crossing on the Selway."

After leaving Pilot Creek, the road became rough and steeper, crossing mountains, spiny ridges, and gigantic slides of granite rock. Marty's top speed pulling the horse trailer on the best stretches of the road was twenty miles per hour. Mostly though, fifteen miles per hour was the rule.

Tom's head bobbed and nodded as he dozed in the comfort of the last rays of an afternoon sun. Marty was lost deep in thought. He remembered the fishing trip on Newsome Creek when his grandfather first told him of the Magruder murders and the lost gold. He remembered his grandfather telling him about Lloyd Magruder's letter to his wife and how he had read it. How that letter had spurred him on to search for the gold.

Marty wondered why he hadn't searched out Howard Williams before. He could have found the letter years ago. He supposed living life dimmed that memory and finding the artifacts last year resurfaced the conversation that he had with his grandfather. *When was that?* he said to himself. *In 1957, I believe. The same year Grandpa killed the record moose.*

Marty smiled to himself as he remembered other events on that day of the conversation. He recalled, with a shiver, that he pointed his new .22 rifle at George Timick's back with the full intention of shooting him if he had harmed his grandpa. He remembered seeing that his grandfather was okay and then quietly returning to camp and replacing the .22, so his grandfather wouldn't know that he had found it before his birthday. He laughed aloud when he recalled his thoughts, thinking he had fooled his grandfather about the gun and pointing it at Timick. Lloyd Rupp's words were still vivid in his mind: "Before you go gettin' too surprised, do you need to unload your gun?" He laughed again when he remembered how his grandfather told him that he knew he was on the rock pile behind Timick, pointing his rifle at his back.

While ago on thet rock pile, ye were quiet all right, but yer shadow gave ye away. Remember how I showed ye 'bout yer shadow when yer a-fishin' a stream? Well, same applies, if yer a-huntin' man or beast. Marty remembered that lesson and applied it years later, in Vietnam.

He missed his grandfather and wished that he could be here with him now.

"Wouldn't he be proud," Marty said aloud.

"What's that?" Tom asked, just awake from his snooze.

"Oh, nothing," Marty said. "I was just voicing my thoughts."

"Are we close yet?" Tom asked.

"We are starting the descent into the Selway drainage

now. As I remember, it should take us a half hour. It'll be dark when we get there," Marty said.

They arrived at Magruder Crossing on the Selway right at dark, but there was still enough light to make a quick camp, picket and feed the horses.

Marty slept a sound sleep that night, but he dreamed. He dreamed the same dream he did as a young boy on Newsome Creek, except this time it wasn't George Timick carrying an axe. It was Simon Wick, with a menacing smile that displayed a missing front tooth.

Soon after midnight, a small Datsun pickup drove slowly by Marty and Tom's camp. Normally, a vehicle with a dislodged tail pipe would have awakened either one of them, but the past day had been log and exhausting. They both remained fast asleep.

Inside the pickup, the doorman was arguing with Simon. "I don't want to hurt nobody, Simon. I don't want to be here and find gold. I want to go home and do my job at the hotel. You should go home, too, and be with Becky. Treat her nice."

"Shut up, you lamebrain," Simon shouted. "If it wasn't for me, you'd be nothing, a nobody. Now drive down the road a ways and we'll find another place to camp. In the morning, we'll ask our friends with horses where they are going. Could be they will give us a ride into the mountains."

"I don't want to ride horses, Simon," the doorman protested.

"Listen, you stupid fool. If I told you once, I've told you ten times, one of those guys is Marty Kincade. His name was on the tool box and his name is in this damn magazine. He's the private investigator who found the Magruder artifacts. Hell, he probably knows where the gold is. The guy who wrote the magazine article sure seems to think so. Now, shut up. I'm doing this for you, too. If we find that gold, we'll both be rich forever."

"You're gonna kill them, Simon. I don't wanna kill nobody. I wanna go home."

"You stupid ass. I'm gonna kill you if you don't shut your mouth. I'm sick and tired of listening to you. Now shut up." With that, Simon pulled a .38 snub-nose revolver from his waistband and put the barrel into the doorman's ear. "You feel this, Doorman? You little piece of shit. I mean it. Do as I say or I'll shoot you right now and throw you in the river. Now pull off the road up ahead. It looks like a camping spot right where your headlights are shining."

The doorman did as instructed, but he didn't like it. For the first time in his life, the doorman felt real hard anger. Not fear, humiliation, or hurt feelings, just plain anger.

When they parked, the doorman laid his head on the steering wheel. "I'm sleeping here," he said.

"Suit yourself, Home Boy," Simon replied, "but I'm getting my sleeping bag out and stretch out on the ground. It's too cramped to sleep in here, as you'll find out."

"I don't care," the doorman said. "I don't want to be by you. You're mean."

"Do what you damn well please, but give me your car keys."

The doorman started to object, but remembered Simon's gun. He removed the keys from the ignition and tossed them to Simon.

"Sleep tight, Home," Simon said, as he left the pickup and removed his sleeping bag from the rear.

In ten minutes, he was fast asleep. The doorman wouldn't sleep at all. He was preoccupied with his new-found anger.

At 5:00 A.M., Marty was awakened by the sun. He woke Tom up and they ate a quick breakfast of oatmeal and apples. Marty then watered and saddled the horses while Tom cleaned their few dishes.

By 6:00 A.M., they were one mile up Magruder Ridge, off the Selway. Their camp and vehicles looked like toys at this height, Tom commented, as they dismounted to rest the horses. Far below and up river from them, Marty spotted the orange Datsun pickup of the doorman's.

At the same moment Marty and Tom were watching the Datsun with binoculars, the doorman left his vehicle and started to urinate in some nearby bushes. He looked over to another clump of bushes and saw Simon as he squatted for his morning nature call. After he finished urinating, the doorman walked over to the front of his pickup, bent down, and obtained his spare ignition key. He then got back in his pickup, started it up, and drove off.

It would be another seventeen hours before the doorman would lie down and go to sleep in his bed at Portland, but when he woke up, no one would ever call Billy Gilbert the doorman again.

"Well, for hell's sake, they're leaving!" Marty shouted, as he watched the orange Datsun drive slowly away and start the ascent into the Bitterroots.

"Wonder why they would drive deep into the wilderness over these kind of roads, then decide to go back," Marty stated, as he continued to watch the Datsun climb the adjacent mountain.

"Guess maybe when they woke up this morning, the scenery scared them," Tom said.

"Oh, well. That's one less worry for us. Let's get on up to the massacre site. It's only another mile."

Far below, next to the river, Simon Wick also watched the departing Datsun. In his right hand, he held his .38 snub nose. In his left, a roll of toilet paper. His pants were down around his ankles and his face red with rage. He watched the Datsun until it disappeared from view. Then he realized that his pants were still down. He quickly pulled his pants up and considered his options. There was really only one: follow Marty Kincade up that mountain, if he hadn't left already.

Simon went to Marty's camp and realized immediately that he was too late, but then he saw horse tracks in the soft riverbank. They appeared to be heading toward that steep ridge directly across the river from their camp. Simon felt he had no other choice, so he waded the shallow river and started climbing the ridge. *This must be Magruder Ridge.* He thought. *How in hell do people get horses up a steep son of a bitch like this?* Before long, Simon could see the horse tracks going up the ridge. The horses left a noticeable plowed trail in their climbing efforts. He checked the rounds in his revolver. "I'm going to kill those bastards," he said to himself.

He continued to climb, but he was having great difficulty. Simon was not in good shape and these mountains were difficult to travel, even for the best woodsman.

As Simon climbed higher, the air became thinner. His breathing became rapid, as he sucked in air for his tortured lungs. He slipped and fell often on the dry pine needles that carpeted the ground. Twice he fell on sharp rocks and tore his pants and skin.

Simon was hurting, hot and thirsty. He was also enraged and he was directing that rage at Marty Kincade and Tom Haugstad. All of his ills were their fault. Simon was no longer thinking with reason. He was a man propelled by raging anger and greed.

On the ridge top, Marty and Tom had been working for nearly an hour. Marty had found the hole in the rocks from last year, and he and Tom worked to enlarge it so they could drop into the space below.

"Gad, what's that smell?" Tom asked, as he stuck his head and shoulders into the hole.

"Wood rat," Marty said, "I smelled him last year when I

first opened this hole."

"That means there is another opening then," Tom said, "because he didn't get in there by the hole we dug."

"It's on the other side of this ridge. Saw it before we started to dig. But if we tried to follow him, we would have had all rock to dig through."

"Our hole is big enough to get through," Marty said. "Want to join me? This is the moment of real adventure."

"Thanks, but no thanks," Tom said. "I don't like holes. I'll have my adventure from up here."

"Suit yourself," Marty replied. "Let me borrow your pen light. I might need more light than just mine." As Marty slipped into the hole, Tom handed him his pen light. Just as quickly, Marty's head disappeared below the ground surface.

For a few moments, Marty couldn't see much until his eyes became accustomed to the darkness.

The first thing he noticed was the size of the space. He had dropped into a very dry, musty-smelling, rock-walled room, about eighty feet in length and nearly thirty feet wide. The next thing he saw were the wooden boxes. He approached them, illuminating them with the pen lights. As he got closer, he could make out the word "Dynamite" on the sides of the boxes. "Damn," he swore.

"What's the matter?" Tom asked from above.

"These boxes say 'dynamite' on the sides."

"Be careful. I don't want to get blown off this ridge."

"Don't worry," Marty said. "I don't want you blown off this ridge either."

Marty peeked inside one of the boxes and saw the gold. He checked another, then another. All were filled with gold and gold ore. "Hot damn. Bingo. We hit the jackpot, Tom. The gold is in the dynamite boxes."

"Well, I'll be damned," came the reply from above.

The next thing Marty saw, was the partially dirt covered

skeleton of a man lying on the ground next to the dynamite boxes. "I think maybe I found Lloyd Magruder," Marty yelled up at Tom.

Instantly, Tom was on his hands and knees, with his head poking through the hold. "Let me see," he said. "Put the light on him." Marty did and moved to the side so Tom could get a better look. "Holy shit. Look at that axe cut in his skull," Tom said.

Marty hadn't noticed that. He was looking at what was partially buried in the dust beneath the skeleton's ribs. Marty picked it up. It appeared to be round and metal, although it was badly tarnished. Marty scraped it with his knife, then rubbed it on his shirt. He could see that the object was silver and there appeared to be some kind of writing on the top. He rubbed it on his shirt, more vigorously this time. He looked at the object. The initials "L.M." were clearly visible. "Lloyd Magruder," Marty said softly. He then used his knife to pry the object open. As it opened, Marty saw that it was two things. The lower thicker part was a very old watch. The top part was a picture of a woman, probably Caroline Magruder.

Marty was in awe and totally engrossed in his find, until he felt something crawl across his boot toe. He illuminated it and saw the biggest timber rattler he had ever seen. Marty respected rattlesnakes, but he wasn't terrified of them. He quickly put his toe on the snake's head and pinned it to the ground. The snake immediately started rattling and twisting its body around Marty's ankles. Marty put the L.M. watch into his pocket and reached down and grabbed the snake behind the head with one hand and the tail with the other. He noted the rattler was probably three feet long and two inches thick. As Marty was admiring the reptile, he yelled up to Tom, "Hey, Tom, I have a snake down here. You want 'em?"

"No thanks," Tom replied. "I've got one up here."

"No, seriously, Tom. I really do have a snake down here."

"I'm serious, too," Tom said. "Better poke your head up here or this snake is gonna bite me, he says."

Wondering, Marty bent over, walked to the hole, and poked his head out through the top. Standing a few feet away was Tom with his hands raised and standing in front of Tom stood Simon Wick, with a revolver in his hand, pointed at Tom. Wick was breathing heavy, his clothes were dirty and torn, and his Princeton hairstyle was all disarrayed, but he was smiling his toothless grin.

"I thought you left us," Marty said.

"You saw the chicken shit doorman leave, but that's okay. It means more gold for me," Simon boasted. "Now where is the gold?"

"It's down here in this hole, but you will never get it out by yourself."

"That's okay. I'm not going to do it by myself. You and your friend here can help me."

"And if we don't?" Marty asked.

"Well, then, I'll just bury you in that hole. Your horses will help me do what I need to do."

"So if we help you, will you let us go?" Marty asked.

Simon turned to him and grinned his toothless grin. Marty hurled the rattler at him and the snake landed on his chest, then fell at his feet. The snake quickly coiled and struck, burying its fangs into his right calf. Simon recoiled, with terror and fired six shots at the again coiling snake. One round struck the snake two inches below its head and it died in seconds.

Simon dropped his gun and pulled his pant leg up. Two little blue puncture marks, a quarter inch apart, were visible on his white calf. "Oh, God," he said, "help me."

"Help yourself, you son of a bitch," Tom shouted. "I'm going to finish what the snake started." He then reached down and picked up a shovel.

Simon yelled and threw his gun down. "I'm unarmed," he said.

"Good. It'll be easier to kill you then," Tom replied.

Simon turned to run, but fell. When he did, a book slid from under his shirt and landed on the ground.

He regained his feet and started running down the ridge from where he had come. In seconds, he was out of sight.

Tom looked over at Marty. "Why didn't you shoot him?" he asked.

"I didn't bring my gun. It's still in the Blazer. Why didn't you shoot him?"

Tom looked at the ground. "Mine's in the Blazer, too."

Marty climbed out of the hold and sat on a rock. After a while Tom came over and sat beside him. "Well, now what, chief?"

Marty thought for a long time. "The cat's out of the bag. I doubt if we can get any gold out before the Forest Service finds out. Loudmouth down there will probably go up to the Ranger Station for medical attention, so I guess we'd just as well go too. I'll have the ranger there radio to Missoula and get Bill Fox down here. He'll want to investigate this and I'm sure he'll be happy I didn't take any artifacts this time."

"How far is the Ranger Station from our camp?" Tom asked.

"About two miles, so we'll have a little time. I saw two or three very large chunks of what looked like pure gold lying on the ground down there. They aren't part of any human activity, so I guess we can take them. Maybe, if I go to court, I'll get more, but I guess I'd better do it legally."

"What's that you've got?" Marty asked, as Tom picked a book from the ground.

"I don't know. I saw Wick drop it when he took off running. My God! It says 'Journal II, Property of John Wick 1861.'"

"What?" Marty said. "Maybe we had better read that. John Wick was this jasper's kin of some kind and I believe he was Lloyd Magruder's partner in the Elk City store. He left after the murder but returned a few times looking for this gold."

They spent the next hour reading and when they were finished, they left Magruder Ridge and didn't even talk. They led the horses. When they arrived at the river, they saw the body of Simon Wick, face down in water, stuck on a sand bar.